Attention-Deficit/Hyperactivity Disorder in Children and Adolescents

D1591754

About the Authors

Brian P. Daly, PhD, is assistant professor of psychology and director of practicum training at Drexel University, Philadelphia, PA. Dr. Daly has authored or coauthored two books, 26 research articles, and 20 book chapters related to child psychopathology, pediatric chronic illness, and school mental health.

Aimee K. Hildenbrand, MS, is a doctoral student in the clinical psychology program at Drexel University, Philadelphia, PA. She is a student advisory board member for the Society of Pediatric Psychology (APA Division 54) and is a graduate student representative of the SPP Hematology/ Oncology/Bone Marrow Transplant Special Interest Group.

Ronald T. Brown, PhD, ABPP, is the president of the University of North Texas at Dallas and professor of psychology. Previously he served as the provost and senior vice president for academic affairs at Wayne State University in Detroit, MI. He has provided leadership for a variety of national associations.

Advances in Psychotherapy – Evidence-Based Practice

Series Editor
Danny Wedding, PhD, MPH, School of Medicine, American University of Antigua, St. Georges, Antigua

Associate Editors
Larry Beutler, PhD, Professor, Palo Alto University / Pacific Graduate School of Psychology, Palo Alto, CA
Kenneth E. Freedland, PhD, Professor of Psychiatry and Psychology, Washington University School of Medicine, St. Louis, MO
Linda C. Sobell, PhD, ABPP, Professor, Center for Psychological Studies, Nova Southeastern University, Ft. Lauderdale, FL
David A. Wolfe, PhD, RBC Chair in Children's Mental Health, Centre for Addiction and Mental Health, University of Toronto, ON

The basic objective of this series is to provide therapists with practical, evidence-based treatment guidance for the most common disorders seen in clinical practice – and to do so in a reader-friendly manner. Each book in the series is both a compact "how-to" reference on a particular disorder for use by professional clinicians in their daily work and an ideal educational resource for students as well as for practice-oriented continuing education.

The most important feature of the books is that they are practical and easy to use: All are structured similarly and all provide a compact and easy-to-follow guide to all aspects that are relevant in real-life practice. Tables, boxed clinical "pearls," marginal notes, and summary boxes assist orientation, while checklists provide tools for use in daily practice.

Attention-Deficit/ Hyperactivity Disorder in Children and Adolescents

Brian P. Daly
Department of Psychology, Drexel University, Philadelphia, PA

Aimee K. Hildenbrand
Department of Psychology, Drexel University, Philadelphia, PA

Ronald T. Brown
Office of the President, University of North Texas, Denton, TX

 hogrefe

Library of Congress Cataloging in Publication information for the print version of this book is available via the Library of Congress Marc Database under the Library of Congress Control Number 2014959626

Library and Archives Canada Cataloguing in Publication
Daly, Brian P., author
    Attention-deficit/hyperactivity disorder in children and adolescents / Brian P. Daly (Department of Psychology, Drexel University, Philadelphia, PA), Aimee K. Hildenbrand (Department of Psychology, Drexel University, Philadelphia, PA), Ronald T. Brown (Office of the President, University of North Texas, Denton, TX).

(Advances in psychotherapy--evidence-based practice ; v. 33)
Includes bibliographical references.
Issued in print and electronic formats.
ISBN 978-0-88937-412-6 (pbk.).--ISBN 978-1-61676-412-8 (pdf).-- ISBN 978-1-61334-412-5 (html)

    1. Attention-deficit hyperactivity disorder. 2. Attention-deficit hyperactivity disorder--Diagnosis.
3. Attention-deficit hyperactivity disorder--Treatment. 4. Attention-deficit disorder in adolescence.
5. Attention-deficit disorder in adolescence--Diagnosis. 6. Attention-deficit disorder in adolescence--Treatment.
I. Hildenbrand, Aimee K., 1989-, author II. Brown, Ronald T., author III. Title. IV. Series:
Advances in psychotherapy--evidence-based practice ; v. 33

RJ506.H9D34 2015   618.92'8589   C2015-900414-4
                                                C2015-900415-2

Cover image © Imgorthand – istockphoto.com

© 2016 by Hogrefe Publishing
http://www.hogrefe.com

PUBLISHING OFFICES
USA: Hogrefe Publishing Corporation, 38 Chauncy Street, Suite 1002, Boston, MA 02111
                Phone (866) 823-4726, Fax (617) 354-6875; E-mail customerservice@hogrefe.com
EUROPE: Hogrefe Publishing GmbH, Merkelstr. 3, 37085 Göttingen, Germany
                Phone +49 551 99950-0, Fax +49 551 99950-111; E-mail publishing@hogrefe.com

SALES & DISTRIBUTION
USA: Hogrefe Publishing, Customer Services Department,
                30 Amberwood Parkway, Ashland, OH 44805
                Phone (800) 228-3749, Fax (419) 281-6883; E-mail customerservice@hogrefe.com
UK: Hogrefe Publishing, c/o Marston Book Services Ltd., 160 Eastern Ave.,
                Milton Park, Abingdon, OX14 4SB, UK
                Phone +44 1235 465577, Fax +44 1235 465556; E-mail direct.orders@marston.co.uk
EUROPE: Hogrefe Publishing, Merkelstr. 3, 37085 Göttingen, Germany
                Phone +49 551 99950-0, Fax +49 551 99950-111; E-mail publishing@hogrefe.com

OTHER OFFICES
CANADA: Hogrefe Publishing, 660 Eglinton Ave. East, Suite 119-514, Toronto, Ontario, M4G 2K2
SWITZERLAND: Hogrefe Publishing, Länggass-Strasse 76, CH-3000 Bern 9

Hogrefe Publishing
Incorporated and registered in the Commonwealth of Massachusetts, USA, and in Göttingen, Lower Saxony, Germany

Printed and bound in the USA

ISBN 978-0-88937-412-6 (print) • ISBN 978-1-61676-412-8 (PDF) • ISBN 978-1-61334-412-5 (EPUB)
http://doi.org/10.1027/00412-000

Acknowledgments

We sincerely thank those children and adolescents with ADHD, and their families, for allowing us into their lives whether through clinical work or research studies. It has been our privilege to work with amazing young people and caregivers and to witness their resilience in the face of continuing challenges. We have learned many important lessons from them, and their experiences continue to inspire us.

Dr. Daly wishes to thank his parents for instilling the values of compassion and hard work, his wife, Kristin, for her continued love and support, and his sons Leo and Colt for all their smiles.

Aimee Hildenbrand wishes to express her sincere gratitude toward her family, partner, mentors, and colleagues for their unwavering support and encouragement.

Dr. Brown wishes to thank Denise, for her love and encouragement over the past 2 years.

Table of Contents

1

Description

1.1   Terminology

Attention-deficit/hyperactivity disorder (ADHD) is a neurodevelopmental disorder marked by persistent patterns of inattention and/or hyperactivity-impulsivity symptoms that emerge during childhood and are functionally impairing across settings. *The Diagnostic and Statistical Manual of Mental Disorders*, Fifth Edition (DSM-5; American Psychiatric Association, 2013) assigns the following codes for this disorder:

314.01 Attention-Deficit/Hyperactivity Disorder, Combined Presentation
314.00 Attention-Deficit/Hyperactivity Disorder, Predominantly Inattentive Presentation
314.01 Attention-Deficit/Hyperactivity Disorder, Predominantly Hyperactive/Impulsive Presentation
314.01 Other Specified Attention-Deficit/Hyperactivity Disorder
314.01 Unspecified Attention-Deficit/Hyperactivity Disorder

The *International Classification of Diseases*, 10th Edition, Clinical Modification (ICD-10-CM; World Health Organization [WHO], 2014) lists ADHD under codes F90.9 "Attention-Deficit Hyperactivity" and F90.0 "Attention-Deficit without Hyperactivity." First described in the medical literature in the late 1700s (Barkley & Peters, 2012), ADHD-related symptoms were previously referred to by numerous labels including "minimal brain damage," "minimal brain dysfunction," "hyperkinetic impulse disorder," "hyperactive child syndrome," "hyperkinetic reaction of childhood," and "attention deficit disorder," among others (Taylor, 2011). Changes in terminology have generally reflected evolving theoretical conceptions based on symptoms of the disorder and its management.

1.2   Definition

According to the DSM-5, ADHD is "a persistent pattern of inattention and/or hyperactivity-impulsivity that interferes with functioning or development" (American Psychiatric Association, 2013, p. 61), as defined by the following diagnostic criteria listed in Table 1.

Table 1
DSM-5 Diagnostic Criteria for ADHD

A. [Either] (1) and/or (2):

1. **Inattention:** Six (or more) of the following symptoms have persisted for at least 6 months to a degree that is inconsistent with developmental level and that negatively impacts directly on social and academic/occupational activities. **Note**: The symptoms are not solely a manifestation of oppositional behavior, defiance, hostility, or failure to understand tasks or instructions. For older adolescents and adults (age 17 and older), at least five symptoms are required.

  a. Often fails to give close attention to details or makes careless mistakes in schoolwork, at work, or during other activities (e.g., overlooks or misses details, work is inaccurate).

  b. Often has difficulty sustaining attention in tasks or play activities (e.g., has difficulty remaining focused during lectures, conversations, or lengthy reading).

  c. Often does not seem to listen when spoken to directly (e.g., mind seems elsewhere, even in the absence of any obvious distraction).

  d. Often does not follow through on instructions and fails to finish schoolwork, chores, or duties in the workplace (e.g., starts tasks but quickly loses focus and is easily sidetracked).

  e. Often has difficulty organizing tasks and activities (e.g., difficulty managing sequential tasks; difficulty keeping materials and belongings in order; messy, disorganized work; has poor time management; fails to meet deadlines).

  f. Often avoids, dislikes, or is reluctant to engage in tasks that require sustained mental effort (e.g., schoolwork or homework; for older adolescents and adults, preparing reports, completing forms, reviewing lengthy papers).

  g. Often loses things necessary for tasks or activities (e.g., school materials, pencils, books, tools, wallets, keys, paperwork, eyeglasses, mobile telephones).

  h. Is often easily distracted by extraneous stimuli (for older adolescents and adults, may include unrelated thoughts).

  i. Often forgetful in daily activities (e.g., doing chores, running errands; for older adolescents and adults, returning calls, paying bills, keeping appointments).

[A] 2. **Hyperactivity and impulsivity:** Six (or more) of the following symptoms have persisted for at least 6 months to a degree that is inconsistent with developmental level and that negatively impacts directly on social and academic/ occupational activities. **Note**: The symptoms are not solely a manifestation of oppositional behavior, defiance, hostility, or a failure to understand tasks or instructions. For older adolescents and adults (age 17 and older), at least five symptoms are required.

  a. Often fidgets with or taps hands or feet or squirms in seat.

  b. Often leaves seat in situations when remaining seated is expected (e.g., leaves his or her place in the classroom, in the office or other workplace, or in other situations that require remaining in place).

  c. Often runs about or climbs in situations where it is inappropriate. (**Note**: In adolescents or adults, may be limited to feeling restless).

  d. Often unable to play or engage in leisure activities quietly.

  e. Is often "on the go," acting as if "driven by a motor" (e.g., is unable to be or uncomfortable being still for extended time, as in restaurants, meetings; may be experienced by others as being restless or difficult to keep up with).

  f. Often talks excessively.

Table 1 (continued)

g. Often blurts out an answer before a question has been completed (e.g., completes people's sentences; cannot wait for turn in conversation).

h. Often has difficulty waiting his or her turn (e.g., while waiting in line).

i. Often interrupts or intrudes on others (e.g., butts into conversations, games, or activities; may start using other people's things without asking or receiving permission; for adolescents and adults, may intrude into or take over what others are doing).

B. Several inattentive or hyperactive-impulsive symptoms were present prior to age 12 years.

C. Several inattentive or hyperactive-impulsive symptoms are present in two or more settings (e.g., at home, school, or work; with friends or relatives; in other activities).

D. There is clear evidence that the symptoms interfere with, or reduce the quality of, social, academic, or occupational functioning.

E. The symptoms do not occur exclusively during the course of schizophrenia or another psychotic disorder and are not better explained by another mental disorder (e.g., mood disorder, anxiety disorder, dissociative disorder, personality disorder, substance intoxication or withdrawal).

Specify whether:

314.01 (F90.2) Combined presentation: If both Criterion A1 (inattention) and Criterion A2 (hyperactivity-impulsivity) are met for the past 6 months.

314.00 (F90.0) Predominantly inattentive presentation: If Criterion A1 (inattention) is met but Criterion A2 (hyperactivity-impulsivity) is not met for the past 6 months.

314.01 (F90.1) Predominantly hyperactive/impulsive presentation: If Criterion A2 (hyperactivity-impulsivity) is met and Criterion A1 (inattention) is not met for the past 6 months.

Specify if:

In partial remission: When full criteria were previously met, fewer than the full criteria have been met for the past 6 months, and the symptoms still result in impairment in social, academic, or occupational functioning.

Severity current severity:

Mild: Few, if any, symptoms in excess of those required to make the diagnosis are present, and symptoms result in no more than minor impairments in social or occupational functioning.

Moderate: Symptoms or functional impairment between "mild" and "severe" are present.

Severe: Many symptoms in excess of those required to make the diagnosis, or several symptoms that are particularly severe, are present, or the symptoms result in marked impairment in social or occupational functioning.

The diagnostic criteria für ADHD according to ICD-10-CM are listed in Table 2.

Table 2
ICD-10 Diagnostic Criteria for ADHD

Behavioral and emotional disorders with onset usually occurring in childhood and adolescence (F90–F98)

F90 Hyperkinetic disorders
A group of disorders characterized by an early onset (usually in the first five years of life), lack of persistence in activities that require cognitive involvement, and a tendency to move from one activity to another without completing any one, together with disorganized, ill-regulated, and excessive activity. Several other abnormalities may be associated. Hyperkinetic children are often reckless and impulsive, prone to accidents, and find themselves in disciplinary trouble because of unthinking breaches of rules rather than deliberate defiance. Their relationships with adults are often socially disinhibited, with a lack of normal caution and reserve. They are unpopular with other children and may become isolated. Impairment of cognitive functions is common, and specific delays in motor and language development are disproportionately frequent. Secondary complications include dissocial behavior and low self-esteem.

Excl.:
Anxiety disorders (F41.-)
Mood [affective] disorders (F30–F39)
Pervasive developmental disorders (F84.-)
Schizophrenia (F20.-)

F90.0 Disturbance of activity and attention
Attention deficit:
– Disorder with hyperactivity
– Hyperactivity disorder
– Syndrome with hyperactivity
Excl.:
Hyperkinetic disorder associated with conduct disorder (F90.1)

F90.1 Hyperkinetic conduct disorder
Hyperkinetic disorder associated with conduct disorder

F90.8 Other hyperkinetic disorders

F90.9 Hyperkinetic disorder, unspecified
Hyperkinetic reaction of childhood or adolescence NOS
Hyperkinetic syndrome NOS

Reprinted with permission from the *International Statistical Classification of Diseases and Related Health Problems*, 10th Revision, Version for 2014, © 2014 World Health Organization. Retrieved from http://apps.who.int/classifications/icd10/browse/2014/en#/F90 on January 16, 2015.

1.3   Epidemiology

1.3.1   Prevalence and Incidence

3–10% of school-aged children and 2–6% of adolescents have ADHD

Among the most commonly diagnosed mental health disorders, ADHD is estimated to affect between 3% and 10% of school-aged children and 2–6% of adolescents (Raishevich-Cunningham & Jensen, 2011). A meta-analysis that pooled rates of ADHD across countries suggested a 1-year global prevalence rate of 5.3% in children and adolescents (Polanczyk, de Lima, Horta, Biederman, & Rohde, 2007). There has been widespread concern from the general public lay press as well as by some in the scientific community that rates of ADHD have increased over time. Nonetheless, evidence suggests that the significant variability in prevalence estimates over the past 3 decades is primarily accounted for by heterogeneous study methodologies (Polanczyk, Willcutt, Salum, Kieling, & Rohde, 2014). In particular, studies vary greatly in their sampling techniques, diagnostic criteria, and informants, among other factors. With regard to incidence, findings from a carefully designed study conducted by Barbaresi and colleagues (2002) suggested that the cumulative incidence of ADHD is approximately 7.5% among school-aged children.

1.3.2   Sex

ADHD is diagnosed more frequently in males than in females, with an estimated ratio of 2:1 or higher (Polanczyk et al., 2007). However, this sex difference may be a result of older diagnostic criteria that were developed with predominantly male samples. Additionally, girls are more likely to present with primarily inattentive features and less likely to exhibit overt comorbid conduct problems as compared with their male counterparts, which may account for markedly higher treatment referral rates among boys. Perhaps due to more careful identification of specific subtypes (primarily inattentive) over the past decade, there has been a significant increase in the prevalence of ADHD among females (Barkley, 2006). While ADHD is more common among boys, research suggests that both groups experience significant functional impairments in academic performance, comorbidity with learning disorders (LDs), and social problems (Hinshaw et al., 2012).

ADHD is more frequent in males than females

1.3.3   Age

ADHD typically emerges early in childhood and is most commonly identified during the elementary-school years, when symptoms become more evident and impairing, particularly in academic settings. In preschool-aged children, this disorder primarily manifests as excessive motor activity. While ADHD may be diagnosed in very young children, as suggested in the DSM-5, hyperactivity symptoms are particularly difficult to differentiate from normative behaviors for children below the age of 4 years (American Psychiatric Association, 2013). Inattention appears to become more prominent during elementary school. During adolescence, hyperactivity symptoms tend to shift from overt motoric signs (e.g., running, climbing) to more subtle symptoms including fidgetiness, restlessness, or impatience. A substantial proportion of children with ADHD continue to exhibit symptoms into adulthood that result in impairments across settings and situations (American Psychiatric Association, 2013).

1.3.4   Ethnicity

ADHD occurs across all nationalities and cultures

While prevalence rates and diagnostic practices vary across countries, there is little doubt that ADHD occurs across all nationalities and cultures. Polanczyk and colleagues (2007) found that prevalence was highest in South America (11.8%) and Africa (8.5%) and lowest in the Middle East (2.4%). However, after controlling for variability in diagnostic and assessment methods across studies, these differences were not significant. Furthermore, in geographical regions with sufficient data available for narrow confidence intervals (i.e., North America, Europe, Oceania, Asia), prevalence rates of ADHD were similar (3.7–6.3%). Further, there is evidence for a consistent two-factor ADHD symptom structure across cultures for school-aged children, thereby supporting the validity of this disorder (Bauermeister, Canino, Polanczyk, & Rohde, 2010). Nevertheless, there is preliminary research to suggest that cultures may vary in their interpretation of ADHD-related symptoms. As a result, treatment rates vary widely across countries (Forero, Arboleda, Vasquez, & Arboleda, 2009). Additional research is needed to better understand the cultural variation in the identification and management of ADHD and its related symptoms.

1.4   Course and Prognosis

As previously noted, the onset of ADHD symptoms typically occurs during early childhood. Preschool-aged children who exhibit inattentive and hyperactive behaviors for 1 year or more are likely to be diagnosed with ADHD and to continue to display symptoms into school-age and adolescent years (Olson, Bates, Sandy, & Lanthier, 2000). From childhood to adolescence, inattention becomes more prominent, whereas hyperactivity tends to shift from impulsive, disinhibited behavior to feelings of restlessness or impatience. A considerable proportion of children with ADHD (i.e., between 50% and 80%) continue to meet criteria for this disorder into adolescence as well as adulthood (American Psychiatric Association, 2013) again attesting to the validity of the disorder across the lifespan. Greater child oppositional and defiant behavior, parent–child conflict, and maternal negativity predict persistence of ADHD symptoms from preschool into childhood and adolescence (Olson et al., 2000). If left untreated, ADHD can result in significant impairment and often results in poor academic achievement, higher rates of school dropout, a higher frequency of auto accidents, impaired social functioning and self-regulation, lower adaptive and self-care capacities, and compromised occupational outcomes in children with ADHD relative to their peers without the disorder (Barkley, 2006; Lee, Lahey, Owens, & Hinshaw, 2008). For example, individuals with ADHD are more likely to drop out of high school and less likely to complete college. In addition, they are more apt to be employed in lower paying jobs relative to their education. Approximately one quarter or more (25–45%) of children with ADHD also will meet criteria for conduct disorder (CD), and a significant subset are at higher risk for substance use or abuse in adulthood (Mannuzza & Klein, 2000).

ADHD frequently persists into adulthood

Given that ADHD is a chronic disorder that places children at risk for a variety of negative psychosocial outcomes, it is important that appropriate treatment be initiated as early as possible and that it address multiple domains of functioning and be continuously evaluated over time (see Chapter 4 for further discussion of treatment). While some intensive treatment programs have demonstrated success in reducing ADHD and oppositional defiant and internalizing symptoms, as well as increasing social skills, parent–child relations, and school achievement, as compared with control conditions, these effects appear to dissipate by 1 year following treatment cessation (Molina et al., 2009). Furthermore, presentation or intensity of treatment for ADHD does not appear to predict functioning 6 to 8 years later, whereas early ADHD symptom trajectory accounts for more than half of clinical outcomes later in childhood or adulthood (Molina et al., 2009). Thus, even with intensive treatment, most children with ADHD continue to display symptoms through adolescence and adulthood, thereby leading many professionals to suggest that the diagnosis of ADHD indeed carries a guarded prognosis.

1.5   Differential Diagnosis

ADHD is a disorder in which young people exhibit signs and symptoms that are also present in a number of other psychiatric and/or medical conditions, which can make differential diagnosis challenging even for the experienced practitioner (see Table 3). The categories in which symptomatic overlap occur most frequently include emotional or behavioral conditions (e.g., anxiety, depressive, oppositional defiant, and conduct disorders), neurological or developmental disorders (e.g., learning and language disorders or other neurodevelopmental disorders), physical or medical conditions (e.g., tics, lead poisoning, sleep apnea), and psychosocial or environmental factors (e.g., stressful home environment, trauma, parental psychopathology, ineffective schooling). Because these conditions may mimic or be comorbid with ADHD, the clinician should consider alternative explanations and, if appropriate, diagnose each condition separately, because each diagnosis may require a specific mode of treatment. In the case of a comorbid condition, the clinician should determine which of the coexisting conditions is primary or secondary (e.g., disorders that are exacerbated by the ADHD), as this will influence treatment decisions. Finally, clinicians should consider how cultural factors influence symptom presentation and how these cultural factors may affect management of ADHD.

ADHD is often comorbid with other psychiatric disorders and medical conditions

1.5.1   Behavioral Conditions

ADHD combined presentation and ADHD predominantly hyperactive/impulsive presentation share some common core characteristics and symptom patterns such as impulsive behavior, interrupting or intruding on others, and difficulty waiting one's turn, with disruptive behavioral disorders such as oppositional defiant disorder (ODD), CD, and intermittent explosive disorder (IED). Because ODD and CD are the most common comorbid conditions associated with ADHD, clinicians should assess for ADHD when a child presents with ODD or CD. When considering a diagnosis, practitioners should also be

ADHD, ODD, and CD share some common core characteristics

Table 3
Overlapping Symptoms Between ADHD and Other Psychiatric Disorders

ADHD	ODD	Conduct disorder	Depression	Anxiety	OCD	Adjustment disorder	Bipolar disorder	PTSD	Substance use/ abuse
Inattention symptoms									
Fails to give close attention to details or makes careless mistakes in schoolwork			X						
Trouble holding attention on tasks or play activities			X	X	X	X		X	X
Does not seem to listen when spoken to directly			X						
Does not follow through on instructions and fails to finish schoolwork or chores			X				X		X
Trouble organizing tasks and activities			X						
Loses things necessary for tasks and activities			X						
Easily distracted			X				X		X
Forgetful in daily activities			X						X
Hyperactivity and impulsivity symptoms									
Fidgets with or taps hands or feet, or squirms in seat				X			X		
Leaves seat in situations when remaining seated is expected							X		
Runs about or climbs in situations where it is not appropriate	X								

Table 3 (continued)

ADHD	ODD	Conduct disorder	Depression	Anxiety	OCD	Adjustment disorder	Bipolar disorder	PTSD	Substance use/abuse
Unable to play or take part in activities quietly									
Often "on the go" acting as if "driven by a motor"				X			X		X
Talks excessively							X		
Blurts out an answer before a question has been completed							X		
Has trouble waiting his/her turn	X	X							
Interrupts or intrudes on others	X	X							
Nondiagnostic associated characteristics									
Labile Mood							X	X		X
Low self-esteem				X			X		X	
Temper outbursts	X	X						X	X	
Demoralization				X					X	
Dysphoria				X						X (during withdrawal)

Note. OCD = obsessive-compulsive disorder; ODD = oppositional defiant disorder; PTSD = posttraumatic stress disorder.

aware that young people with ADHD and comorbid ODD or CD frequently display more severe hyperactive-impulsive symptoms compared with children with ADHD alone (Newcorn et al., 2001). What makes differential diagnosis especially difficult is that there may be isolated instances of the symptoms of ODD and CD in an ADHD child. Thus, the astute practitioner should make certain that the symptom patterns are excessive for the developmental level of the child and that the symptom threshold for ADHD or ODD/CD is met according to ratings of frequency, severity, and impairment across settings and activities as detailed in the DSM-5 or ICD-10.

1.5.2   Emotional Conditions

Symptoms of ADHD may overlap with emotional conditions or mood disorders

Difficulties with sustained attention, maintaining concentration, and avoiding distraction are symptoms of ADHD that may overlap with emotional conditions or mood disorders such as depressive disorder, anxiety disorder, reactive attachment disorder, bipolar disorder, disruptive mood dysregulation disorder (DMDD), and posttraumatic stress disorder (PTSD). Practitioners are likely to encounter young people who believe, or whose caregivers believe, that the child suffers from ADHD when in fact the child may be experiencing symptoms associated with a mood disorder. For instance, adolescents with depression may exhibit impaired concentration and trouble paying attention at school, while a child with PTSD may demonstrate impulsivity. Therefore, when making a differential diagnosis, clinicians should be aware of any constitutional predisposition toward problems with symptoms of inattention and impulsivity and for some overactivity as well as the early onset and long course history of the disorder. In contrast, when these symptoms are associated with depression or anxiety, they tend to be more transient in nature and are temporally related to the onset of the mood disorder.

1.5.3   Neurological or Developmental Conditions

ADHD symptoms overlap with numerous specific neurodevelopmental disorders

Neurodevelopmental disorders that either share symptoms or are comorbid with ADHD include intellectual disability, specific LDs, language or communication disorders, autism spectrum disorders (ASDs), neurodevelopmental syndromes (e.g., fragile X, phenylketonuria [PKU]), seizure disorder, and motor coordination disorders (e.g., stereotypic movement disorder). Specific LDs and language or communication disorders share a number of the overt ADHD symptoms such as difficulty following instructions or shifting from one uncompleted task to another. However, these symptoms are more directly connected to the LD or language or communication disorder as the core issue to be resolved. Thus, when children receive specialized educational interventions that improve their ability to read, such as in the case of dyslexia, an additional benefit may be that the child becomes more attentive and better able to follow instructions. Frequently, many children who receive a diagnosis of ADHD have a comorbid LD (Larson, Russ, Kahn, & Halfon, 2011). Properly diagnosing each disorder is critically important because the management of the two disorders differs: The management of a specific LD involves various

ADHD is frequently comorbid with learning disorders

cognitive and special educational or remedial approaches, and the treatment of ADHD may require behavioral management and/or medication.

Symptom patterns and characteristics associated with ADHD that may overlap with ASDs, neurodevelopmental syndromes, seizure disorder, and motor coordination disorders include cognitive impairments (e.g., inattention, disorganization, executive dysfunction), behavioral challenges (e.g., hyperactivity and impulsivity), and difficulty establishing and maintaining peer relationships. Differential diagnosis of ADHD from neurodevelopmental disorders may require specialized testing – for instance, taking a thorough history, observations of behavior across settings and situations, and administering psychoeducational or neuropsychological testing are standard for distinguishing ADHD from a specific LD or an ASD. It is noteworthy that the DSM-5 now recognizes that ADHD can be diagnosed as comorbid with an ASD (American Psychiatric Association, 2013). This represents a change from the *Diagnostic and Statistical Manual of Mental Disorders,* 4th Edition, Text Revision (DSM-IV-TR; American Psychiatric Association, 2000), in which the diagnosis of ADHD was prohibited when an underlying pervasive developmental disorder was present (American Psychiatric Association, 2000). Genetic testing is often recommended for neurodevelopmental syndromes such as fragile X or PKU. An electroencephalography (EEG) is used to determine the presence of a seizure disorder, whereas a comprehensive occupational therapy evaluation can assist in the diagnosis of a motor coordination disorder.

1.5.4   Environmental and Psychosocial Factors

ADHD is a disorder in which the manifestation of symptoms is contingent on the environment in which the disorder occurs. Stressful home environments or an inappropriate educational setting do not cause ADHD; however, these environmental factors may contribute to the expression of inattentive, hyperactive, or impulsive behavior. One factor that can help differentiate the contribution of these factors relative to ADHD is the impact of the behavior in different settings. For example, children who live in unstructured, stressful home environments are more likely to demonstrate negative behaviors at home but not at school, while those young people in an inappropriate educational setting are more likely to demonstrate challenging and inattentive behaviors at school but not at home. In contrast, children with ADHD typically display these negative behaviors across multiple settings (e.g., home and school).

Several psychosocial factors that may complicate a diagnosis of ADHD include child trauma (neglect, physical or sexual abuse), bullying (victim or perpetrator), recent significant stressors (death or separation from a relative), parent–child temperament mismatch, poor attachment with caregivers, parental dysfunction (inconsistent or harsh discipline), and parental psychopathology or substance abuse. For example, studies have found that mothers with depression are more likely to report higher levels of ADHD symptoms on rating scales (Chi & Hinshaw, 2002). On the other hand, parenting a child with ADHD is also associated with maternal depression and higher levels of stress relative to parents of children without ADHD (for a review, see Johnston & Mash, 2001). In both instances, the use of multiple informant ratings (e.g.,

Multiple informant ratings across settings aid in the diagnostic process

caregivers, teachers) across settings can help clarify whether the child meets criteria for ADHD.

1.5.5   Physical and Medical Conditions

There are a number of physical and medical conditions whose symptom presentation may resemble ADHD, including sleep disorders (e.g., obstructive sleep apnea, restless-leg/periodic limb movement disorder, delayed sleep phase syndrome), lead poisoning, low birth weight, fetal alcohol syndrome, thyroid irregularities (hypothyroidism and hyperthyroidism), and visual or hearing impairments. In addition, the adverse side effects of certain medications such as Albuterol, a medication used to manage asthma, may mimic some of the symptoms of ADHD (Pearl, Weiss, & Stein, 2001). Lastly, some of the sequelae (e.g., impaired concentration) associated with the use and/or abuse of substances may present in a fashion similar to that of ADHD. Some of the key differential characteristics between these conditions include the symptom fluctuation associated with disease course or adverse effects of medication as compared with the relatively stable, pervasive, and persistent symptom presentation associated with ADHD.

> **Side effects of some medications may resemble symptoms of ADHD**

1.6   Comorbidity

The presence of a single or even multiple comorbid disorders is often the norm rather than the exception for those young people who present for evaluation and treatment of ADHD at mental health clinics, with estimates as high as 80% for the presence of at least one additional mental health disorder (Kadesjo & Gillberg, 2001). However, there is significant variability in prevalence estimates of comorbidity depending on gender, stage of development (childhood vs. adolescence), and whether the study was conducted in a community or clinic setting. Therefore, the prevalence rates described for the different conditions below represent averages of rates across sexes, developmental levels, and different settings.

> **Comorbid conditions are the norm rather than the exception for young people with ADHD**

The disorders that fall in the disruptive or externalizing behavior problems domain are the conditions that most frequently co-occur with ADHD. For example, ADHD is comorbid with ODD in 40% of children, and co-occurs with CD in 15% of young people with ADHD (Waschbusch, 2002). Approximately 25% of young people with ADHD also have a comorbid specific LD (Larson et al., 2011). The prevalence rate for anxiety disorders that include separation anxiety disorder and generalized anxiety disorder is about 25% in young people with ADHD (for a review, see Nigg & Barkley, 2014). Estimates are lower for mood disorders (including DMDD), with about 15% of young people with ADHD also having one or more of these comorbid conditions. The prevalence rate for comorbidity with tic disorders is 15%, while the rate is 5% for ASDs. Finally, rates of co-occurring substance use disorders (SUDs) in adolescents and young adults is 15%, while approximately 30% of young people with ADHD have symptoms of sleep disorders (for a review,

> **Disruptive or externalizing behavior problems are the disorders that most frequently co-occur with ADHD**

see Nigg & Barkley, 2014). Consequently, it is important for practitioners to understand and evaluate for comorbid psychiatric, learning, developmental, substance use, and sleep disorders that occur with ADHD, as these conditions may dictate other treatment interventions that may be necessary, or they may suggest specific treatment management for ADHD.

Although not officially listed as a disorder in the DSM-5, there has been significant clinical interest and research on sluggish cognitive tempo (SCT) and potential relationships of this syndrome with ADHD. The core symptoms of SCT include sluggishness/sleepiness, apparent "daydreaming," being easily confused, and seeming unmotivated. Although initially believed to be a subtype of ADHD – usually associated with the inattentive type – there is general consensus that SCT is a distinct disorder that is not specific to ADHD (for a review, see Nigg & Barkley, 2014). For example, young people with SCT often present with more internalizing problems (e.g., depression, anxiety) and demonstrate a pattern of social withdrawal that differs from the social intrusion often seen in children with ADHD. In addition, compared with that in children with ADHD, the rate of disruptive behavior disorders is much lower in children with SCT. Moreover, processing speed and reaction times are decidedly slower in young people with SCT compared with their peers with ADHD. Even taking into account these emotional, behavioral, and cognitive differences, study results indicate that SCT coexists with ADHD in about 35–50% of cases (Barkley, 2012; Bauermeister, Barkley, Bauermeister, Martinez, & McBurnett, 2012).

Sluggish cognitive tempo coexists with ADHD in about 35–50% of cases

1.6.1   Oppositional Defiant Disorder or Conduct Disorder

Children with ADHD and a comorbid disruptive or externalizing behavior disorder such as ODD or CD are often described as overreacting to events, situations, or rules that others would judge as relatively minor. In essence, transitioning to new activities or situations tends to pose major problems for children with ADHD. Their reactions may include yelling, having a temper tantrum, refusal to obey rules, or in more extreme cases, escalating to violent behavior such as physical aggression. These behaviors are often characterized as extreme relative to the precipitant. While some refusal of rules or parental requests are a normal part of development, children with ADHD and a comorbid disruptive behavior disorder consistently struggle with self-regulation and engage in this type of reactive behavior over a sustained period of time. It appears that the presence of ODD and CD is more common in children with the combined or hyperactive/impulsive presentations of ADHD (Gadow et al., 2004).

ODD and CD are more common in children with the combined or hyperactivity/ impulsivity presentations of ADHD

1.6.2   Anxiety

Children with co-occurring anxiety disorders and ADHD are often described as "worriers." Unlike children who only have ADHD, children who have both an anxiety disorder and ADHD demonstrate explicit symptoms of anxiety, and they exhibit undue concerns about their skills and performance in social situations, athletics, and academic settings. These children may also display high levels of worry about the safety of their parents or other family members, what people think about what they say or do, and their behavior in activities or at events. Practitioners should be alert for behavioral signs of anxiety in children who present with ADHD, such as motor tension, separation anxiety, nervous mannerisms, and speech abnormalities. There is some evidence to suggest that girls with ADHD are more likely than boys with ADHD to be diagnosed with a comorbid anxiety disorder – often in the form of separation anxiety disorder (Levy, Hay, Bennett, & McStephen, 2005). It is important to note that although parents and teachers are considered to be more accurate informants regarding children's observable externalizing behaviors and symptoms associated with ADHD, children are often better sources of information regarding symptoms of internal states (anxiety, depression, self-esteem).

> **Practitioners should be alert for behavioral signs of anxiety in children who present with ADHD**

Children with comorbid anxiety disorders may be more likely to demonstrate impaired social functioning and problems at school, but show no difference in academic performance relative to children with ADHD alone. Although anxious ADHD youths are less likely to struggle with disruptive behavior problems, they are also more likely to experience stressful life events than those children with only ADHD. Studies from the early 1990s suggest that children with comorbid anxiety and ADHD derived fewer cognitive and behavioral benefits from stimulant medications and reported a greater frequency of adverse side effects from the stimulants than did their peers who were identified as having ADHD without such comorbidities. However, more recent studies, including the Multimodal Treatment Study of Children with ADHD (MTA; MTA Cooperative Group, 1999) and an investigation by Abikoff and colleagues (2005), found no association between anxiety and stimulant response. Because the appropriate management of either ADHD or anxiety can have a positive effect on the child's functional outcomes (e.g., academic performance, peer socialization), clinicians should routinely assess for the possible presence of symptoms associated with anxiety in children where the diagnosis of ADHD has been made.

1.6.3 Mood

> **Symptoms of ADHD are associated with impaired emotional regulation, motivation, and arousal**

Various mood disorders such as major depressive disorder, dysthymic disorder, and DMDD can also co-occur with ADHD (Larson et al., 2011). Symptoms of ADHD are associated with impaired emotional regulation, motivation, and arousal. In addition, children with ADHD frequently exhibit rapid mood alterations and often do not demonstrate awareness of the triggers affecting these changes. Because of these rapid changes, individuals with ADHD who have comorbid depression may endorse depressive symptoms, but report that the depression has not been consistent most of the day for 2 weeks or more. Another common symptom of children with ADHD where there is significant comorbidity of depressive symptoms is a tendency to inflate the importance of difficult events and to have little control over the effects of stress. Thus, these children may exhibit irritability, anger, and social dysfunction in relation to their ADHD symptoms.

To form a diagnosis of comorbid ADHD and depression, clinicians need to carefully assess whether individuals experience a consistently depressed affect for 2 weeks or more. It is noteworthy that persons with ADHD and depression may be at greater risk for accidents and suicidal behavior than individuals with only one of these disorders. Hence, the astute practitioner should always be vigilant for the presence for suicidal ideation, gestures, or behaviors. Young people with ADHD who are being managed with stimulant medication may also have problems associated with the adverse side effects of these medications that include loss of appetite, anxiety, dysthymia, insomnia, physical complaints, and irritability. It is especially noteworthy that of the nine DSM-5 criteria for depression, six of these symptoms overlap with the adverse effects associated with stimulant medication. These symptoms include decreased interest or pleasure in most activities, change in appetite, change in sleep (insomnia), change in activity (psychomotor agitation or retardation), feelings of guilt or worthlessness, fatigue or loss of energy, and poor concentration. Because of the overlap between depressive symptoms and the adverse effects of stimulant medication, the course of symptom development may be the most useful way of differentiating between ADHD, treatment with stimulant medication, and the possibility of depression.

1.6.4   Bipolar Disorder

Bipolar disorder is a psychiatric disorder that has been increasingly recognized in children and adolescents and also is increasingly being diagnosed as a comorbid condition in young people with ADHD. The differential diagnosis between bipolar disorder and ADHD can be especially difficult because there are specific symptoms that are similar in both disorders that include a high level of energy, restless behavior, impatience, impulsive speech, trouble focusing, and reduced need for sleep. One of the key differentiators is the elated mood, grandiosity, and mood swings of the bipolar child that come in episodes and then dissipate for several weeks or even months such that they alternate with relatively normal mood levels. Additional distinguishing characteristics between the disorders are that children and adolescents with ADHD display symptoms that are generally present early in life, follow a chronic course, and are always present, while bipolar disorder most often manifests itself in adolescence or young adulthood and is much more variable with regard to presentation.

The differential diagnosis between ADHD and bipolar disorder is difficult due to symptom overlap

1.6.5   Learning Disorder

The symptoms of ADHD can cause a child to struggle in school; however, poor school performance may also be due to a specific LD. In those cases where LD is comorbid with ADHD, it is most often associated with the inattentive or combined presentations of ADHD. Some research suggests that weaknesses in working memory and executive functions are present in comorbid LD and ADHD (for a review, see Nigg & Barkley, 2014). In addition, Tannock and Brown (2000) observe that some children with ADHD and LD appear to be fidgety and inattentive, and may have difficulty following complex conversations. They also note that academic performance for these children often seems slow and inaccurate in children with comorbid ADHD and LD, whereas cognitive performance for children with ADHD alone is rapid and inaccurate, most often due to impulsive and careless errors.

When LDs are comorbid with ADHD, the most common association is with inattentive or combined presentations of ADHD

1.6.6   Tics and Autism Spectrum Disorders

Children with ADHD are at higher-risk of tics than their healthy peers

Children with ADHD are more likely than their typically developing peers to have tics, with signs of ADHD typically appearing before the onset of tics (Bloch, Panza, Landeros-Weisenberger, & Leckman, 2009). The behavioral impulsivity associated with ADHD is sometimes confused with the vocal or motoric impulsivity that can be present in tics. Relative to children who only have tic disorders, young people with co-occurring ADHD and tic disorders experience greater functional impairment and report lower quality of life (Eddy et al., 2011). Although some concerns have been noted regarding tic exacerbation from the use of stimulant medication, there is no evidence suggesting a causal relationship between the emergence of tics and the initiation of stimulant treatment.

DSM-5 now permits a comorbid diagnosis of ADHD and autism spectrum disorder

As noted previously, DSM-5 now permits a comorbid diagnosis of ADHD and ASD (American Psychiatric Association, 2013). Symptom overlap between the two conditions includes trouble with attention, disorganization, and impulsivity. However, the behavioral expression of these symptoms may differ across conditions. For example, attention problems in children with ADHD are more frequently observed whereby the child encounters difficulty sustaining attention or struggles to stay on task. In contrast, attentional challenges in children with an ASD are more often due to their difficulty in shifting attention away from their narrow range of interests. Thus, children with ASD seem to overfocus their attention on one object, while children with ADHD have difficulty sustaining attention and effort.

1.6.7   Substance Use or Abuse Disorders

Adolescents and young adults with ADHD are more likely to use drugs and alcohol and to develop a substance use disorder compared with their peers

ADHD may pose an especially salient risk for the development of SUDs, and may influence also the recovery from drug and alcohol use. Adolescents and young adults with ADHD are more likely to use drugs and alcohol, to use them at earlier ages, and to develop one or more SUDs than their same same-sex peers without ADHD (Biederman et al., 2006). For example, findings from these studies reveal that the rates of alcohol and substance use for boys with ADHD were 26% and 21%, respectively, as compared with 16% and 11% in boys without ADHD. Findings from another study indicated that the presence of ADHD conferred more than a twofold increase in the vulnerability to develop an SUD across the lifespan (Kessler et al., 2005). Comorbidity of externalizing disorders among children with ADHD also places these young people at greater risk for SUDs, particularly in adolescence.

Some individuals may use substances to medicate their ADHD symptoms. Research has identified several variables that account for increased risk of SUDs in adults with ADHD, including severity of symptoms, ODD and CD comorbidities, temperamental characteristics (frequent temper tantrums), family history of SUD in ADHD, and male gender (Nogueira et al., 2014). Individuals with ADHD tend to abuse drugs more frequently than they abuse alcohol. There is also an interesting association between cigarette smoking and ADHD, with ADHD adolescents being more likely to use cigarettes at an earlier age, become nicotine dependent, and have a more difficult time successfully quitting than their peers who do not have ADHD (for a review, see Lee, Humphreys, Flory, Liu, & Glass, 2011). Individuals with ADHD may also consume caffeine and nicotine in greater quantities than individuals who do not have symptoms associated with the disorder.

1.6.8 Sleep Issues

Children and adolescents with ADHD have greater difficulties with sleep than do their normally developing peers (Corkum, Tannock, Moldofsky, Hogg-Johnson, & Humphries, 2001). These sleep issues are most commonly characterized as difficulty falling and remaining asleep, shorter sleep duration, and challenges with remaining alert throughout the day. Parents often report that their child with ADHD always struggled with falling asleep at night, woke up frequently throughout the night, or encountered difficulties with napping as a preschooler. Some young people with ADHD may also exhibit difficulty waking, even when they obtain an acceptable amount of sleep during the previous night. This difficulty may manifest itself in terms of being late for school or extramural activities. Finally, some young people with ADHD experience daytime sleepiness and as a result have trouble staying alert throughout the day. Many of these children report problems staying awake if they have to sit still for long periods of time or perform routine or boring tasks. Students with ADHD may also report falling asleep in lectures, even when they have had an appropriate amount of sleep. Clinicians may misdiagnose a sleep disorder as ADHD or may even miss sleep disorders among individuals diagnosed with ADHD. Therefore, proper evaluation of sleep disorders in children with ADHD is critical, especially because sleep deprivation or disturbances may give rise to or exacerbate ADHD symptoms. Consequently, all ADHD assessments should include questions regarding sleep routines, daytime sleepiness, and patterns and persistence of sleep difficulties, as well as issues pertaining to sleep hygiene.

> **Sleep routines may be disrupted in children with ADHD**

> **ADHD assessments should include questions that evaluate sleep issues in children**

1.7 Diagnosis

There is no single attentional, educational, medical, or neurological test that can reliably identify ADHD. Therefore, a professional with specific training in ADHD as well as in the identification of other psychiatric disorders should make the diagnosis. This might include clinical or school psychologists, child psychiatrists, developmental/behavioral pediatricians, or behavioral neurologists. Because the disorder is so encompassing and affects both home and academic settings, many professionals use a team approach for the diagnosis or management of the disorder or frequently both. The use of a systematic approach in gathering data across all sources from multiple informants is imperative in accurately diagnosing ADHD. This may include the use of rating forms across settings and situations. Clinical practice guidelines for the assessment and diagnosis of ADHD developed and disseminated by the American Academy of Pediatrics (AAP; Wolraich et al., 2011) and the American Academy of Child and Adolescent Psychiatry (AACAP; Pliszka &

> **No single attentional, educational, medical, or neurological test can reliably identify ADHD**

> **Practitioners should use a systematic approach in gathering data across sources from multiple informants when diagnosing ADHD**

AACAP Work Group on Quality Issues, 2007) share many common goals and recommendations for the assessment process and are described below.

The first step for practitioners in the diagnostic process is to conduct a comprehensive clinical interview with the child and his or her caregivers to obtain information about primary presenting symptoms and problems. This evaluation should include a personal and family history obtained through interviews and observations of the child in at least one setting and at school if at all possible, as well as review of school and medical records and psychological test results. The review of school and medical records is important as there may be indications of hearing, vision, or medical problems as well as behavioral difficulties. The professional should evaluate whether the child meets symptomatic criteria for ADHD according to the DSM-5 or ICD-10. This is best accomplished by asking specific questions about ADHD symptoms while also focusing on gathering information about the onset, frequency, and severity of such symptoms.

During the initial comprehensive interview, the clinician should also assess other possible causes of ADHD symptoms such as anxiety or depression; a situational stressor such as the death of a parent or grandparent or parental divorce; LD resulting in scholastic underachievement; and medical disorders that may affect central nervous system dysfunction, such as temporal lobe seizures. The clinician should also seek to determine whether the classroom or home environments are stressful, chaotic, or lack structure, and if possible the child should be observed in these settings. Such information may provide data with regard to possible stressors that may be causing or exacerbating symptoms and may have important treatment implications.

Another important step in the assessment process is to determine whether other comorbid conditions or disorders (see Section 1.6) coexist with ADHD. As noted previously, in the case of coexisting conditions, the clinician should determine which disorder is primary or secondary in order to inform treatment decisions. In addition, the clinician should generate alternative hypotheses for the differential diagnostic process. Further, it is advised that the clinician determine child and family strengths and assets that may be especially relevant when determining the treatment plan. As is true with the diagnosis of any mental health disorder, clinicians should also consider how cultural factors influence symptom presentation (see Section 4.9 "Multicultural Issues").

One of the most important aspects of the diagnostic process for ADHD is that practitioners obtain information from a variety of measures (e.g., interviews, subjective rating scales, objective testing) and from a variety of sources (e.g., caregivers, teachers, school personnel, or mental health clinicians who work with the child), and across several settings (e.g., home and school). Different strategies for gathering information from the child, caregivers, and teachers are described in more detail below.

Practitioners should gather data from a variety of measures, sources, and across several settings

1.7.1   Diagnostic Interviews

Structured and semistructured instruments help define normal and abnormal behavior

Structured and semistructured interviews conducted with the child and caregivers represent a "top-down" approach to assessment and are most consistent with the criteria listed in the DSM-5. The purpose of using these structured and semistructured instruments in the assessment process is to establish limits between normal and abnormal behavior. This approach is frequently referred to as a categorical approach because it results in a yes/no decision for diagnosis. These interviews are considered the gold standard by psychologists and psychiatrists for assessing psychopathology (Pelham, Fabiano, & Massetti, 2005). However, the use of these interviews is time-intensive and costly, making them difficult to implement in busy clinical settings. Common structured interviews include the Diagnostic Interview for Children and Adolescents-IV (DICA-IV; Reich, Welner, & Herjanic, 2000), and the National Institute of Mental Health (NIMH) Diagnostic Interview Schedule for Children, version 4 (NIMH DISC-IV; Shaffer, Fisher, Lucas, Dulcan, & Schwab-Stone, 2000). Frequently used semistructured interviews include the Schedule for Affective Disorders and Schizophrenia for School-Age Children (K-SADS; Ambrosini, 2000) and the Child and Adolescent Psychiatric Assessment (CAPA; Angold & Costello, 2000).

1.7.2 Rating Scales

The use of standardized behavioral rating scales from caregivers and teachers is recommended in the ADHD assessment process. These rating scales represent an empirically based "bottom-up" approach to assessing symptoms and are referred to as a *dimensional* approach because the scores do not represent a clear delineation of the presence or absence of the disorder. Instead, behaviors or symptoms are assessed along a continuum from normal to abnormal, to assess how the child compares with other children of the same chronological age. Because these scales are usually completed by caregivers and teachers, they can help determine behavioral, peer, or academic problems in the home and school setting. A common narrow band ADHD rating scale is the ADHD Rating Scale (DuPaul, Power, Anastopoulos, & Reid, 1998). The SNAP-IV (Swanson, 1992) and the Vanderbilt ADHD Scales (Wolraich et al., 2003) represent shorter versions of broad-band ADHD scales. Longer broad-band rating scales include the Behavior Assessment System for Children – Second Edition (BASC-2; Reynolds & Kamphaus, 2004), the Achenbach System of Empirically Based Assessment (ASEBA; Achenbach & Rescorla, 2001), and finally the Conners' Rating Scales – Third Edition (Conners 3; Conners, 2008).

> **Standardized behavioral rating scales from caregivers and teachers are very important in the ADHD assessment process**

It is recommended that clinicians not simply assess for symptoms, but also evaluate the level of impairment related to such symptoms. Important domains of impairment that should be assessed include family interactions, peer relationships, and school behavior and academic performance. One way to evaluate these domains is through direct observation or functional behavioral assessments. Parent and teacher rating scales such as the Impairment Rating Scale (IRS; Fabiano et al., 2006) can also be used to assess the degree of ADHD impairment across different settings such as home and school. Again, it must be underscored that to qualify for a diagnosis of ADHD, the child must evidence some degree of functional impairment in at least one setting.

> **It is important that practitioners evaluate for symptoms and the level of impairment**

1.7.3   Psychoeducational Testing

Because young people with ADHD frequently experience impairment in school performance, clinicians should also obtain information about school functioning. Common areas of concern related to the school setting include behavior, peer relationships, and academic performance. Traditional psycho-educational testing may be employed if there are particular concerns about academic skills deficits. In general, the goal of this type of testing is to identify the factors contributing to these problems and then to recommend appropriate strategies and accommodations that will assist the child in realizing his or her potential. These tests often assess cognitive strengths and weaknesses, academic skills, information processing, attention or memory challenges, psychological problems such as anxiety or depression, or some other source or combination of factors. Tests of intelligence and achievement should be given where there is an indication that an LD may be involved. Tests of intellectual functioning may also assist the clinical or school psychologist in determining the presence of intellectual disability, in addition to assessments of adaptive functioning. Tannock and Brown (2000) offer as an illustration, the following steps that should be considered when assessing the possibility of concurrent ADHD and LD:

> **It is important that practitioners evaluate for symptoms and the level of impairment**

1. Attain the child's familial and developmental history for correlates and risks of an LD;
2. Collect teacher and academic ratings of academic progress among multiple academic subject areas;
3. Assess for LDs through recommended methods that might include neuropsychological or traditional psychoeducational assessment;
4. Examine comorbid diagnoses that also might include depression, anxiety, or low self-esteem.

Tannock and Brown (2000) also argue that clinicians should routinely assess for multiple types of LDs in ADHD patients. It is important to underscore that psychoeducational tests are not sufficiently sensitive or specific in identifying ADHD; rather they are useful in the identification of other comorbidities such as developmental deficits including specific LDs or intellectual disability.

> **It is important that practitioners evaluate for symptoms and the level of impairment**

1.7.4   Neuropsychological Testing

No single neuropsychological test is able to reliably identify ADHD in a child or predict response to treatments for ADHD such as stimulant medication (for a review, see Brown & Daly, 2009). However, performance on a combination of neuropsychological tests may yield useful information and therefore comprise an important component of diagnosis for ADHD (e.g., the identification of attentional problems) as well as other comorbidities. In many circumstances, the test results may also help clinicians to identify specific LDs and the need for special education placement. Cognitive impairments in children with ADHD that are often assessed by neuropsychological testing include selective attention, memory, reaction time and information-processing speed, motor speed and visuomotor ability, and executive functions.

> **Performance on neuropsychological tests provides useful information in the diagnosis of ADHD**

Neuropsychological tests that measure attention include the Gordon Diagnostic System (Gordon, 1986), Test of Variables of Attention (TOVA; Greenberg & Waldman, 1993), and Conners' Continuous Performance Test-II (Conners, 2000). Other neuropsychological assessments often include tests of verbal working memory, such as the Digit Span Test (e.g., (Wechsler, 2004), the California Verbal Learning Test (Delis, Kramer, Kaplan, & Ober, 1994), the Sentence Repetition Tests (Lezak, 1995), and the Children's Memory Scale (Cohen, 1997). Other important tests that measure mental flexibility, working memory, and/or executive function include the Wisconsin Card Sorting Test (WCST; Berg, 1948; Grant & Berg, 1948), the Stroop Color-Word Interference Test (Golden, 1978), the Rey-Osterreith Complex Figure (Osterrieth, 1944), and the Delis-Kaplan Executive Function System (D-KEFS; Delis, Kaplan, & Kramer, 2001). Finally, tests that evaluate multiple abilities include the Developmental Neuropsychological Assessment – Second Edition (NEPSY-II; Korkman, Kirk, & Kemp, 2007) and the Cambridge Neuropsychological Test Automated Battery (CANTAB; Robbins et al., 1994). Some of these neuropsychological tests are discussed in greater detail in Chapter 3.

1.7.5   Laboratory Testing

Laboratory, physiological, radiological, or neurological testing is not indicated in the context of unremarkable medical history for ADHD. While evoked potentials, genetic testing, and functional brain imaging have been used in research studies of children with ADHD, these tests still lack well-defined clinical utility. Quantitative EEG measures have demonstrated some validity, but questions remain about utility and feasibility for diagnostic use for children with ADHD.

Laboratory, physiological, radiological, or neurological testing is not indicated in the context of an unremarkable medical history for ADHD

2

Theories and Models of ADHD in Children and Adolescents

2.1   Neurobiological Factors in ADHD

2.1.1   Genetic Contributions

Familial, twin, and adoption studies consistently suggest that genes play an important role in the etiology of ADHD. Reviewing 20 twin studies from the United States, Australia, Scandinavia, and the European Union, Faraone and colleagues (Faraone et al., 2005) found a mean heritability index of 76%. In other words, approximately three quarters of the variability in ADHD can be accounted for by genes, rendering it among the most heritable of psychiatric disorders. Despite this marked degree of heritability, molecular genetic studies suggest that the genetic architecture of ADHD is extremely complex. Genetic linkage studies, in which DNA markers are examined to determine whether chromosomal regions are shared more often than would be expected among ADHD family members, are scarce and have produced inconsistent findings. On the other hand, candidate gene studies have provided compelling evidence to suggest that several genes may be involved in the etiology of ADHD. Meta-analyses suggest associations between ADHD and the dopamine D4 and D5 receptor genes, the dopamine β-hydroxylase gene, the synaptosomal-associated protein 25 gene, and the serotonin transporter and 1B receptor genes, as well as somewhat weaker associations with the dopamine transporter gene (Faraone & Mick, 2010). However, these associations are relatively weak, and none of the genes investigated to date have proven sufficient or essential in causing ADHD (Kieling, Goncalves, Tannock, & Castellanos, 2008). Together with the variability in genetic linkage studies, these findings suggest that genetic vulnerability to ADHD is mediated by multiple genes of weak to moderate effects interacting with environmental factors (Faraone & Mick, 2010; Tripp & Wickens, 2009).

Genes play a prominent role in the etiology of ADHD

2.1.2   Neurological Factors

Structural and functional neuroimaging studies have identified key neurophysiological differences between individuals with and without ADHD that support a neurological basis for this disorder. In particular, investigations have consistently documented that children with ADHD have smaller brain regions including the corpus callosum, caudate nucleus, cerebellar vermis, and right frontal cortex as compared with healthy comparison children (Cortese et al.,

2012; Kieling et al., 2008). Additionally, children with ADHD have reduced cerebral volumes affecting all four major lobes. Empirical evidence suggests that these structural volume differences are present early in childhood, are not explained by pharmacological treatments and do not appear to be progressive, although they persist through adolescence. These findings suggest that genetic contributions and early neurological insult may account for structural brain differences in ADHD.

In addition to structural brain alterations, functional neuroimaging studies have revealed that children with ADHD compared with healthy controls have different activation patterns during tasks requiring attention and inhibition. A recent meta-analysis by Cortese and colleagues (2012) suggests hypoactivation in a number of brain regions among children with ADHD, including the frontal-parietal and ventral attention networks, which support goal-directed executive processes, and decision making as well as attentional orientation to behaviorally relevant stimuli, respectively. Furthermore, children with ADHD exhibit hypoactivation in the right somatomotor system, supplementary motor area, and putamen, which may help to explain motoric hyperactivity in ADHD. Young people with ADHD also show increased activation in regions associated with the default network (i.e., structures that are typically active when at rest). The default network supports processes that are typically suppressed during external tasks that demand attention. The default-mode theory of ADHD suggests that the default network may be inadequately regulated and thereby disrupts cognitive performance during tasks requiring sustained attention.

Overall, converging findings from neuroimaging research have identified the primary anatomic regions and basic circuitry underlying the pathophysiology of ADHD: the right prefrontal cortex, basal ganglia, and cerebellum (Cortese et al., 2012). More specifically, ADHD appears to involve alterations in: (1) frontal-limbic/striatal circuits that are instrumental in behavioral and emotional regulation and impulse control, (2) frontal-parietal-subcortical circuits, including the dorsal and ventral attention streams involved in attention and concentration, and (3) the default-mode network, which appears to function abnormally among individuals with ADHD. Together, these findings provide evidence for theories of ADHD that integrate multiple neural circuits and pathways. For instance, Nigg and Casey (2005) proposed an integrative theory of ADHD involving the interplay among circuits involved in cognitive control, emotion regulation, motivation, and attentional capture. In particular, these researchers posited that the frontal-striatal and frontal-cerebellar neural loops are instrumental in predicting *what* and *when* important events in the environment will occur; these circuits interact with the frontal-limbic circuits to designate emotional significance to these events as well as the frontal-parietal-subcortical circuits (attentional capture, alertness, suppression of competing stimuli; Nigg & Casey, 2005). In young people with ADHD, these fundamental circuits develop and operate abnormally, resulting in poorer cognitive and affective control, learning, and other mental operations mediated by the prefrontal cortex.

More recently, it has been suggested that the default network may provide additional avenues for understanding the neurobiology of ADHD (Cortese et al., 2012; Sonuga-Barke & Castellanos, 2007). The default network comprises a series of brain regions (i.e., medial and lateral parietal cortex, medial prefrontal cortex, posterior cingulate cortex) that tend to demonstrate *decreased*

Many children with ADHD have structural brain differences relative to their peers

The right prefrontal cortex, basal ganglia, and cerebellum are implicated in the pathophysiology of ADHD

neural activity during most goal-directed activities (Shulman et al., 1997). According to the default-mode network hypothesis of ADHD, these brain regions may be inadequately regulated by systems active during task engagement and thereby disrupt ongoing cognitive performance, resulting in fluctuations in attention that are characteristic of ADHD. Using the relatively new technique of resting state functional connectivity magnetic resonance imaging (rs-fcMRI), which assesses spontaneous correlations of activity throughout the brain during rest, recent research has provided initial support for this theory. In particular, findings suggest that children with ADHD exhibit atypical activation of the default network during task engagement (Cortese et al., 2012). Given its potential associations with executive control and reward processing, the default network has been highlighted as an important target for future investigation to reveal the potential pathophysiology of ADHD.

Several theories suggest neurotransmitter dysfunction in children with ADHD

Lastly, several theories of ADHD involve neurotransmitter dysfunction, particularly in dopamine pathways (Tripp & Wickens, 2008). These theories were initially sparked by observations of dramatic responses to stimulant medication among children with ADHD. Most stimulants act by altering the availability of dopamine at the synapses and by affecting noradrenergic pathways. Tripp and Wickens (2008) developed a theory of dopamine transfer deficit (DTD) to explain the symptoms of ADHD. In particular, these researchers suggest that in normally developing children, dopamine cell response to positive reinforcement transfers to previously neutral cues that predict reinforcement; this process provides an anticipatory dopamine signal that delivers immediate and continued cellular reinforcement when behavioral reinforcement is delayed. In children with ADHD, however, the anticipatory transfer of dopamine cells to the cue that predicts reinforcement does not occur normally. As a result, children with ADHD may exhibit delayed dopamine signaling and less effective reinforcement at the cellular level. Research over the past decade has advanced our understanding of the impact of stimulant medications on neuronal components implicated in ADHD, yet additional research is needed to better understand the potential role of dopaminergic and noradrenergic pathways in the development and manifestation of this disorder among children (for a more thorough review, see Swanson, Baler, & Volkow, 2011).

2.1.3   Cognitive Determinants

Children with ADHD exhibit impaired executive function

Considerable neuropsychological research has demonstrated differences between children with and without ADHD on various neurocognitive tasks. Nigg and Casey (2005) noted that the greatest deficits exhibited by those with ADHD fall within the following domains: vigilance-attention, cognitive control or executive functions, and motivation. Executive functions encompass a range of higher-order control processes that activate, integrate, prioritize, and manage other neuropsychological functions. Several executive functions appear to be impaired among children with ADHD – namely, response inhibition, vigilance, working memory, and planning (Tripp & Wickens, 2009). Likewise, children with ADHD demonstrate deficits in motivation, particularly as related to response to reinforcement. For instance, there has been some research to suggest that children with ADHD exhibit difficulty delaying gratification, often preferring smaller, immediate reinforcements over larger, delayed reinforcements, although subsequent studies have not always supported this notion. Preference for immediate reinforcers appears to be associated with hyperactivity and inattention within the classroom. Given the importance of dopamine in the neural circuits underlying reinforcement, these findings may lend support to the DTD theory of ADHD (Tripp & Wickens, 2008).

Many theoretical models of ADHD proposed over the past century have been derived from these neurocognitive differences. Among the most influential of these theories is Russell Barkley's (1997) model of ADHD, which centers on behavioral inhibition. According to Barkley's original theory, poor behavioral inhibition is the central deficiency in ADHD and is responsible for deficits in other executive functions – namely, nonverbal and verbal working memory (i.e., ability to retain and manipulate information), affect or emotional and motivational self-regulation, and planning and problem solving. When intact, these executive functions are believed to enable self-regulation. In ADHD, however, Barkley argues that these executive functions are impaired, thereby producing the hallmark and secondary symptoms associated with the disorder. Based on research advances, Barkley amended his initial theory by adding self-awareness or self-directed attention as a central deficit alongside inhibition (Barkley, 2012). Barkley's theory has proven useful and influential in that it has stimulated extensive research on executive functions, emphasized the relevance of specific types of executive functions to ADHD, and inspired additional more cohesive and integrated theories of ADHD.

Russell Barkley's model is a useful formulation of ADHD

2.2   Environmental Risk Factors

Although genetics account for 70–80% of the risk in susceptibility to ADHD (Biederman & Faraone, 2002), there are a number of environmental factors, including prenatal, perinatal, and postnatal exposures and complications, toxins, dietary factors, and psychosocial adversity factors, which may be associated with the ADHD phenotype. While these factors are not necessarily causal, they are associated with or may exacerbate a constitutional predisposition to the disorder or its symptoms.

There are a number of environmental risk factors associated with ADHD

2.2.1   Prenatal, Perinatal, and Postnatal Factors

Prenatal biological risk factors include *teratogens*; these are drugs, substances, or conditions that negatively affect prenatal development and may lead to central nervous system dysfunction and behavioral impairments. The teratogens most commonly thought to be associated with the development of ADHD or ADHD symptoms include prenatal maternal smoking, maternal alcohol and illicit substance misuse during pregnancy, viral infections, and maternal stress during pregnancy. In terms of substance use during pregnancy, results from several large prospective studies revealed links between smoking during pregnancy and symptoms of inattention and hyperactivity in affected children (Cornelius & Day, 2009; Galera et al., 2011). Some studies, but not

**Alcohol and
nicotine use during
pregnancy may be
associated with the
development of
ADHD**

all, have detailed a connection between moderate maternal alcohol use during pregnancy and use of illicit substances, on the one hand, and increased risk of symptoms of ADHD, on the other (Knopik et al., 2005; Rodriguez et al., 2009). The evidence is stronger for the link between fetal alcohol spectrum disorders and increased likelihood of ADHD symptoms (Bhatara, Loudenberg, & Ellis, 2006). Findings from several prospective studies support an association between maternal stress during pregnancy and risk of ADHD symptoms in the offspring (Galera et al., 2011; Rodriguez et al., 2009).

**Some children
with ADHD were
premature or had a
low birth weight**

With regard to perinatal factors, several investigations have reported an association between pregnancy complications such as premature birth and low birth weight and an increased risk for inattention and hyperactivity-impulsivity in young people (Galera et al., 2011; Millichap, 2008). However, it should be noted that these complications are found in a relatively small proportion of children with ADHD (American Psychiatric Association, 2000). Postnatal factors associated with ADHD include head trauma (e.g., concussions), especially when the insult impacts the frontal lobes or basal ganglia, and viral infections (e.g., measles, varicella, rubella; Millichap, 2008).

2.2.2   Environmental Toxins

**Some toxins and
organic pollutants
may be risk factors
for the development
of ADHD**

Several toxins and organic pollutants found in the environment are considered to be risk factors but not proven causal factors for the development of ADHD. These factors include contact with high levels of lead during the first few years of life, postnatal organophosphate pesticide exposure, and prenatal exposure to polychlorinated biphenyls (or PCBs; for a review, see Thapar, Cooper, Eyre, & Langley, 2013).

2.2.3   Dietary Factors

**Nutritional
deficiencies,
nutritional surpluses,
and foods high
or low in IgG are
associated with
ADHD**

Factors related to children's diet that are merely associated but not yet empirically supported risk factors for ADHD include nutritional deficiencies (e.g., zinc, magnesium, polyunsaturated fatty acids), nutritional additives (e.g., sugar, artificial food colorings), and foods either low or high in immunoglobulin G (IgG; Thapar et al., 2013).

2.3   Psychosocial Factors

Theoretical perspectives focusing on the association between psychosocial adversity factors and ADHD have addressed indicators such as stress and trauma, prolonged and significant parent–child conflict, and low parental education and socioeconomic status. It should be noted that much of the research on family and psychosocial adversity and ADHD has not clearly proven the direction of the relationship between these factors or adequately controlled for potential confounding variables (Thapar et al., 2013). Therefore, while it is clearly important that practitioners gather information about experiences of childhood adversity, including within families, it is equally important that practitioners understand the limitations of this information in determining causality (including parental blame) or direction of effects related to the development of ADHD. For example, children who suffer from trauma, abuse, or maltreatment have a higher incidence of ADHD (Ford et al., 2000). It must be pointed out, however, that children and adolescents with ADHD are at greater risk for abuse or maltreatment. For instance, an impulsive youngster who is gregarious and risk taking is more apt to be persuaded by an adult to be lured into a situation that places the child or adolescent at risk for abuse or to be a challenging management problem at home, thereby placing him at greater risk for abuse.

Comorbid psychological disorders can arise from child maltreatment

Several studies have provided data to demonstrate that family dysfunction influences the development of ADHD. Knopik et al. (2005) found that both maternal and paternal alcohol dependency increased the likelihood that children would receive an ADHD diagnosis. Parent–child conflict also increases susceptibility for comorbid disorders in childhood, which include ADHD and other externalizing disorders (e.g., CD) that may exacerbate symptoms associated with ADHD (Burt, Krueger, McGue, & Iacono, 2003). Some recent longitudinal and twin studies found that much of the association between parent–child hostility and ADHD is accounted for by confounding inherited factors (Lifford, Harold, & Thapar, 2008, 2009). The one exception to this finding was hostility between mother and son, although much of the association of this and ADHD is driven by the impact of the child's ADHD symptoms on the mother–son relationship. Counts and colleagues (2005) found that inattention and hyperactivity, as identified by caregivers and teachers, were independently associated with children's perceptions of marital conflict. In a longitudinal study of 335 children affected by parental alcoholism, low levels of both intellectual stimulation and emotional support predicted problems associated with inattention and overactivity (Jester et al., 2005).

Family dysfunction may influence the development of ADHD

Finally, there is some evidence to suggest that level of socioeconomic status, including parental education, impact risk for ADHD. For example, St. Sauver et al. (2004) observed an inverse association between parental education levels and risk for ADHD. In addition, findings from several studies affirm the relationship between low socioeconomic status and ADHD symptoms and diagnosis (Froehlich et al., 2007; Langley, Holmans, van den Bree, & Thapar, 2007). Again, while psychosocial adversity factors likely impact the expression of ADHD, there is no definitive evidence to suggest that severity of symptoms plays a causal role in ADHD, and no causal associations can be determined.

2.4 Interactions Among Neurobiological, Environmental, and Psychosocial Factors

The general consensus is that pathways to ADHD are most likely multiple, complex, and diverse. Research over the last 4 decades has provided compelling and consistent support for genetics being the strongest risk factor in the development of ADHD. Findings used to support this conclusion come from

Pathways to ADHD likely involve an interaction among neurobiological, environmental, and psychosocial factors

varied sources that include family, twin, adoption, genome, and candidate gene search studies (Brock, Jimerson, & Hansen, 2009). However, there is also agreement among experts that neurobiological and environmental factors converge with genetics to contribute to the presence of ADHD. More specifically, current thinking in the field suggests that the interaction between genetics and environment differentially impacts neurobiology, which in turn is expressed as symptoms of ADHD (Biederman & Faraone, 2002). The exception to this explanation arises in cases of significant neurological injury such as head trauma or stroke. Current and future research examining the etiology of ADHD will likely continue to focus on the interplay between genetic and environmental contributions and the resulting impact on neurobiological development. Promising and cutting-edge research methodologies that will help us further understand the cause and expression of ADHD include molecular genetics, epigenetics, and neuroimaging.

3

Diagnosis and Treatment Indications

Children are referred for an ADHD evaluation for a variety of reasons, which may include excessive activity levels, trouble following directions or paying attention, poor school performance, disruptive behavior in the home or school setting, challenges with organizing and planning, and trouble with self-regulation of behavior. The most likely referral sources are the child's caregivers, teachers, or primary care pediatrician. Age of referral for evaluation of ADHD in youth may vary from the toddler years to late adolescence. Although diagnostic criteria for ADHD in the DSM-IV-TR required that some symptoms resulting in impairment be present before the age of 7, many studies have refuted the validity of this criterion (for a review, see (Kieling et al., 2010). Findings from these studies suggested that symptoms of ADHD can manifest at later ages, and consequently the latest age of symptom onset to meet the criteria for ADHD in the new DSM-5 has been increased to 12 years (American Psychiatric Association, 2013). Even though the latest age of onset has been extended, symptoms of ADHD usually appear in early childhood, and therefore, it is common for initial evaluations to occur in the younger school-age years (e.g., ages 6–9 years).

> **The most common referral sources are caregivers, teachers, or pediatricians**

> **Most ADHD diagnoses are made during the elementary school years**

Accurately diagnosing ADHD prior to age 6 can be very challenging because symptoms associated with ADHD, such as a short attention span, being overly active, and acting impulsively, can be developmentally appropriate for preschoolers or kindergartners. In addition, some children may be slightly immature for their developmental age, but still behave within normal limits. Moreover, because there are rapid changes in behavioral self-regulation and cognition that occur during the preschool years, it can often be difficult to determine if the current behaviors will persist into later childhood. When children who attend preschool or kindergarten are referred it may be because teachers observe that the child's short attention span is significantly impeding his or her learning or that the child's impulsive and hyperactive behavior has compromised social functioning. Clinicians should pay particular attention to the frequency and severity of the preschool child's behaviors and the extent to which the behaviors interfere with aspects of the child's life such as friendships, school activities, home life, and community activities. Typically, when ADHD is identified during preschool, it is more severe, and the child is more likely to have other psychiatric comorbidities, than when it is identified later in childhood.

> **ADHD diagnosis requires an understanding of age-appropriate behaviors**

Children are more frequently referred for an ADHD evaluation during the early grades of elementary school because of the focus on academic achievement and increased expectations for age-appropriate social functioning that appear during these years (Shepard, Carter, & Cohen, 2000). This period of schooling is typically when independent seat-work is required in the school setting, and children with attentional problems encounter difficulties in academic performance. In addition, behavioral problems such as leaving the seat in the classroom, calling out answers, and interrupting others may also be recognized at this time. When children are referred because of difficulties at school, there are multiple possibilities that may account for these challenges, including ADHD, another disruptive behavior disorder, an internalizing problem, a specific LD or a cognitive impairment (Denckla, 2000). Therefore, assessment for ADHD can present many challenges for the clinician who is frequently tasked with conducting an evaluation that requires differentiating among a multitude of disorders or even identifying a number of comorbidities.

3.1   Assessment Procedures

When conducting a comprehensive evaluation to determine whether a child or adolescent meets criteria for a diagnosis of ADHD, it is recommended that practitioners obtain information from multiple sources (e.g., caregivers and teachers) and across a range of settings (e.g., home and school; Sparrow & Erhardt, 2014). The multimethod assessment should include the following components: (1) a thorough developmental history that includes a focus on behavioral and medical history; (2) clinical interviews with the child, caregivers, and if possible the child's teacher; (3) rating scales or checklists completed by multiple informants for the purpose of capturing a broad perspective with regard to behaviors that may be associated with ADHD across settings; and (4) an evaluation of concurrent psychiatric diagnoses or LDs.

Direct observations of behavior and testing are helpful in the diagnostic process

Other assessment procedures that are more time-intensive but may prove helpful in the diagnostic process include home or school observations and psychoeducational or neuropsychological testing. Direct observations of the child's behavior in the home or classroom setting are useful because they provide a way for the clinician to gain information about symptom expression in naturalistic contexts. Moreover, they capture an array of behaviors that a single office visit may not reveal. While psychoeducational or neuropsychological testing does not identify ADHD, it is useful for identifying other cognitive comorbidities such as specific LDs. The tools discussed in the following sections do not represent an exhaustive list of all available ADHD assessment techniques; instead, these sections examine critical components of an ADHD evaluation and highlight corresponding evidence-based assessment strategies (for a more thorough discussion of specific tests, see Barkley, 2006; Fabiano, 2011; Lee & Humphreys, 2011; Spies, Carlson, & Geisinger, 2010).

3.1.1   General Considerations

The assessment procedure should be structured according to the age of the child, and the diagnostic process ultimately must include assessing whether or not the child meets the DSM-5 or ICD-10 criteria. There are several important issues for clinicians to consider prior to conducting an evaluation of a child suspected of having ADHD. First, it is frequently the case that children with ADHD have limited awareness of their difficulties and the resulting impairment and therefore may even underreport their behaviors. Second, it is often true that different informants whom the clinician may interview do not agree and may also bring their own biases to the assessment setting. For example, the concordance rate between parent and teacher ratings of symptoms of ADHD on behavioral rating scales is modest at best (Wolraich et al., 2004). Third, the symptom expression of ADHD may be variable and dependent on the situation and context. For instance, children who eventually receive the diagnosis of ADHD may actually demonstrate appropriate behavior in the quiet clinicians' offices where there are no distractions or task demands to trigger symptoms. Alternatively, in the classroom setting where there is a high noise level and many opportunities for stimulation and where the demand for on-task behavior is quite high, the child may consistently display symptoms of ADHD.

Parents, teachers, and children may have different viewpoints regarding ADHD symptoms

3.1.2 Developmental History

Information about the child's developmental history can be gained through an interview or through the use of a questionnaire administered to the caregivers. Information that is gathered for the developmental history usually focuses on the following domains: prenatal and perinatal history, developmental milestones, medical history, family history, treatment history, current and past school functioning, current and past social relationships, current behavioral concerns, and other concerns. To best utilize this information in the diagnostic process, clinicians should understand typical attentional development, emotional regulation, and age-appropriate behaviors and social skills. It also is important to note that an unremarkable developmental history does not automatically signify the absence of ADHD; rather a history significant for attentional problems likely suggests the presence of the disorder.

A developmental history can be obtained through interview or caregiver-completed questionnaire

3.1.3 Clinical Interview

Clinical interviews are a key component of all evaluations and are of central importance in diagnosing ADHD and in determining its course and level of impairment. Interviews offer rich, highly descriptive information that goes beyond that obtained through questionnaires, and they provide an opportunity to develop rapport with children and their families (Sparrow & Erhardt, 2014). Additionally, interviews can be used across varied settings with minimal expense. Clinical interviews should assess for all DSM-5 criteria related to ADHD, including the frequency, severity, and persistence of symptoms; age of onset and course; pervasiveness across settings; and associated impairments in functioning, as well as information on differential or comorbid diagnoses. Given that features of inattention, impulsivity, and hyperactivity cut across many disorders, however, it is recommended that interviews be structured such that they are broad and then progressively more narrow in their focus. Assessing broad domains prior to specific ADHD symptoms can facilitate differential diagnosis and yield a more comprehensive understanding of the

Clinical interviews are a mainstay of ADHD diagnosis

young people's functioning. As a result, this interviewing strategy generally enables more accurate diagnoses and thereby more appropriate treatment recommendations (Sparrow & Erhardt, 2014).

Interviews should be conducted with the child, caregivers, teachers, and service providers such as the child's pediatrician to obtain multiple sources of information on presenting problems and functioning across settings. Thus, in formulating an ADHD diagnosis, the clinician must carefully consider multiple sources of information. The practitioner should be aware that information obtained from the different sources during the interview process may be discrepant. For example, the referred child might deny the behavioral problems that parents have observed at home or that teachers may have observed at school. As another example, teachers may report significant problems with the child's ability to pay attention in the structured classroom setting, while the caregivers indicate no problems with the child's attentional control in a home that is characterized by a lack of structure. Alternatively, some clinicians may encounter caregivers who want their child evaluated even though the clinician may ultimately determine no dysfunction other than the child's inability to meet their caregivers' impossibly high standards for academic success or perfection.

Clinical interviews can be conducted with children and caregivers together, or separately

Clinicians may choose to conduct the clinical interview with the child and caregivers present together at the beginning, but then engage in separate interviews if more information is likely to be shared if both parties are not in the room at the same time. In addition to general information about ADHD symptoms, children should be assessed for their subjective experience of symptoms and motivational factors. Interviews with children also provide the opportunity to conduct a mental status exam, collect initial behavioral observations, and discuss parent–child interactions and peer and family relationships. For evaluations with adolescents, the interview should also include conversations with both the youth and caregivers. However, it is more common for clinicians to conduct a separate interview with adolescents as they may be more likely to speak freely when not in the presence of their caregivers. It is critical when evaluating older adolescents that practitioners obtain information about the natural history of the symptoms, as symptoms of ADHD must be present by 12 years of age to qualify for the diagnosis.

Collateral interviews with parents and other caregivers can provide important information regarding a child's functioning at home and in community settings, parenting practices and family expectations, lifestyle factors that may impact symptoms (e.g., nutrition, exercise, sleep), and personal experiences with academic difficulties that may suggest a genetic contribution. Caregivers can also provide information about whether the reported behaviors have been continuous or a response to a temporary situation (e.g., divorce, death of a loved one).

Teachers and other school personnel can provide particularly valuable data regarding a child's functioning in the classroom as compared with same-age peers, academic strengths and weaknesses, and responses to school-based interventions. For example, the clinician may want to know whether the child has trouble waiting his turn, often fidgets or leaves his seat in the classroom, has trouble listening when spoken to, and struggles with following directions and being organized. Teachers are able to provide especially helpful information because they work with many different types of children of the same chronological age and can therefore make comparisons to typical classroom behaviors that require attention and self-control.

In addition to assessing for features of ADHD and other difficulties, clinicians should also assess for exceptions (i.e., instances where the child demonstrates good functioning), which can provide information on the pervasiveness of symptoms and environmental influences (Sparrow & Erhardt, 2014). In some instances (e.g., LDs), ADHD symptoms may be present in a specific context or setting but not others, highlighting the lack of pervasiveness and influence of variables such as modality and content of instruction. Additionally, those instances in which children with ADHD symptoms demonstrate better performance can indicate specific interventions that may be helpful (e.g., structured, engaging, and hands-on instructional environment). Finally, speaking with the child's pediatrician is helpful in ruling out the presence of other health issues (e.g., vision or hearing problems, seizure disorder, exposure to high lead levels) that could be causing ADHD-like symptoms.

Practitioners should assess for times when children do not display ADHD symptoms

3.1.4   Behavioral Rating Scales

Behavioral rating scales are essential elements of evidence-based assessments of ADHD among children and adolescents (Pliszka & AACAP Work Group on Quality Issues, 2007). Their strength is in capturing numerous behaviors simultaneously and providing quantification of the behavior that is normative based. Many standardized rating scales with well-established reliability, validity, and normative data have been developed for assessing ADHD according to DSM-IV criteria (Barkley, 2006). Although rating scales alone are not sufficient for diagnosing ADHD, they do provide useful information regarding a child's functioning relative to age- and sex-matched peers. Additionally, rating scales are convenient and cost-efficient to administer. Initially, it is recommended that broad-band rating scales be administered to examine larger dimensions of child psychopathology (e.g., externalizing and internalizing behaviors; Barkley, 2006), such as the Behavior Assessment System for Children – Second Edition (BASC-2; Kamphaus & Reynolds, 2004) and the Child Behavior Checklist (CBCL; Achenbach & Rescorla, 2001). Both of these rating scales assess internalizing and externalizing symptoms of psychopathology. Subsequently, narrow-band scales should be employed to further evaluate ADHD symptoms. The most commonly used rating scales for evaluating ADHD according to DSM-IV criteria include the Academic Performance Rating Scale (APRS; Barkley, 1990), ADHD Rating Scale-IV (DuPaul et al., 1998), Brown ADD Rating Scales for Children, Adolescents, and Adults (Brown, 2001), Conners' Parent, Teacher, and Adolescent Rating Scales – Third Edition (Conners, 2008), the Home Situations Questionnaire–Revised (HSQ-R) and School Situations Questionnaire–Revised (SSQ-R; Barkley, 1990), and the Vanderbilt Diagnostic Parent and Teacher Scales (Wolraich et al., 2003). Of these, Conners' third edition has been updated to include a scoring option for DSM-5 ADHD criteria.

Beyond their utility for examining psychopathology and ADHD symptoms, questionnaires and rating scales can also provide information on other areas

Behavioral rating scales are a key element of the assessment of ADHD in children and adolescents

relevant for assessment and thereby facilitate appropriate and helpful treatment recommendations. For instance, research suggests that general adaptive behavior (i.e., skills that will assist children in becoming more independent, responsible, and self-sufficient) is impaired among young people with ADHD (Barkley, 2006). Instruments that are commonly employed to assess adaptive behavior include the Vineland Adaptive Behavior Inventory-II (Sparrow, Cicchetti, & Balla, 2005) and the Normative Adaptive Behavior Checklist (NABC; Adams, 1984). Likewise, children with ADHD often display difficulties with social interactions and relationships with peers (Barkley, 2006). While the CBCL and BASC-2 each contain scales that assess children's social behavior, several other instruments provide more detailed information on social skills. The Social Skills Rating System (Gresham & Elliott, 1990) includes both norms and a software scoring program, making it feasible and useful for use in clinical evaluations. Finally, assessments of parent and family factors that can impact ADHD (e.g., parental psychiatric disorders, parental stress, and family discord) may also be useful (see Barkley, 2006, for specific instruments).

3.1.5   Differential Diagnosis and Comorbidities

Practitioners should assess for differential and comorbid conditions when conducting an ADHD assessment

A thorough assessment of differential and comorbid conditions is necessary when conducting an ADHD evaluation. There are several methods that can aid the clinician in gathering this information including the use of broad-band rating scales, structured or semistructured interviews from both caregivers and teachers that allow for the assessments of a broad range of symptoms across settings, and finally the use of direct observations in settings where children and adolescents are likely to demonstrate how they respond to challenges in managing their behavior and emotions. Though early diagnosis may increase the likelihood of effective intervention, misdiagnosis may represent a failure to note difficulties with emotional functioning, child abuse, or learning issues.

3.1.6   Testing

Various tests can be incorporated into ADHD assessments, including tests of intelligence and academic achievement and neuropsychological tests of executive functioning. Although psychoeducational testing is often considered central to a comprehensive ADHD evaluation, Barkley (2006) notes that these tests have not proven effective in detecting ADHD characteristics specifically, nor have they demonstrated utility in accurately classifying the presence of ADHD versus other disorders or no disorder. Research has consistently shown that children with ADHD have lower IQs (about 0.61 standard deviations below the mean) than comparison groups, yet general cognitive deficits are characteristic of many other disorders, and no subtests of intelligence or achievement tests are specific for, or sufficiently sensitive to, ADHD.

Psychoeducational and neuropsychological testing can assist in differential diagnosis

Nonetheless, these tests can provide data to assist in differential diagnosis (e.g., LDs) and in identifying cognitive factors that might contribute to children's symptoms and academic underachievement (Barkley, 2006).

Given that ADHD is associated with impairments in executive functioning (Frazier, Demaree, & Youngstrom, 2004), many neuropsychological tests are also used in the ADHD assessment process. Perhaps the most well-known and commonly used test of executive dysfunction is the WCST (Berg, 1948; Grant & Berg, 1948). Additionally, computerized tests of attention and inhibitory control have become extremely popular in the assessment of ADHD. These continuous performance tasks (CPTs) measure the ability to sustain attention and effort as well as reaction time to stimuli. Additionally, these tests typically yield errors of omission and commission. Errors of omission are believed to be related to inattention, while errors of commission are regarded as an index of impulsivity. Conners' Continuous Performance Test (CPT II; Conners, 2000) and the TOVA (Greenberg & Waldman, 1993) are frequently employed computerized vigilance tasks that provide performance-based information that can be combined with data from clinical interviews, rating scales, and other cognitive tests to assist in assessing and diagnosing ADHD.

An additional advantage of using objective tests as part of a psychoeducational or neuropsychological evaluation is that data from these tests are less influenced by biases than are other sources of information. For example, family members and teachers who complete behavioral rating scales will each have their own expectations and conceptions of normality. Consequently, difficult family relationships can impact caregiver perceptions of symptoms. Similarly, there is evidence that teacher-completed ratings of ADHD are inflated in the presence of other disruptive disorders (e.g., ODD; Abikoff et al., 2002).

> Results from neuropsychological tests are less influenced by bias than subjective reports or rating scales

3.2   The Decision-Making Process

Clinicians should evaluate all of the information gathered during the assessment process to determine whether there is consistent and compelling evidence that a child or adolescent meets diagnostic criteria for ADHD (see Figure 1). In particular, information obtained from clinical interviews, standardized rating scales, and cognitive tests should be integrated to obtain the most comprehensive assessment of a child's or adolescent's functioning, thereby increasing the likelihood of an accurate diagnosis. It should be cautioned that lack of attentional problems on a neuropsychological test does not necessarily rule out the presence of ADHD. Given that assessment environments provide minimal distractions and magnified individualized attention as well as maximum structure, attention problems may be underestimated or undetected by cognitive tests. However, as noted above, psychoeducational and neuropsychological assessment can be useful in identifying comorbidities or provide for differential diagnoses. Finally, some individuals may endorse fewer than six symptoms and thereby fall short of meeting diagnostic criteria. Subthreshhold ADHD may nevertheless impair academic and social functioning and require intervention.

> Subthreshold symptoms can still impact academic and social functioning

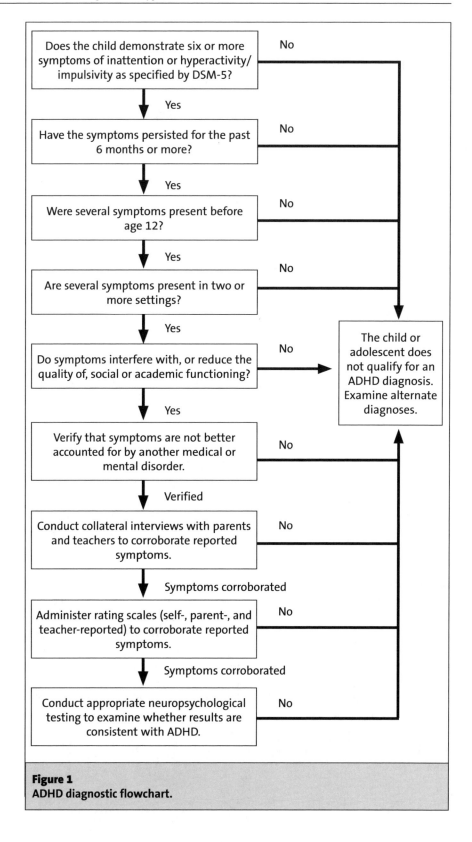

Figure 1
ADHD diagnostic flowchart.

3.3   Treatment Considerations

The ultimate goal of conducting an assessment is to inform treatment. If a child is diagnosed with ADHD, it is important to determine the child's and family's strengths and assets. The clinician also should begin identifying treatment modalities to address symptoms and impairment as well as assess the family's ability to carry out treatment and be compliant with such treatment regimens. Another key aspect of treatment is coordinating resources across settings to establish a continuum of care. The first step in this process should be identifying an appropriate therapist who can advocate the client's needs to the school or work, and in the family environment. A collaboration should be formed between the therapist and a physician or psychiatrist who is able to prescribe medication if this type of therapy is deemed to be necessary. It also is essential that the clinician provide the child and caregivers with education about the nature of ADHD, its management and resources for support. Providing psychoeducation to children and their families can help improve treatment adherence (Corkum, Rimer, & Schachar, 1999), promote satisfaction with treatment (Montoya, Colom, & Ferrin, 2011), and improve functional outcomes (Miranda, Presentacion, & Soriano, 2002).

> Practitioners should identify child and family strengths/ assets when deciding on a treatment modality

Some children with ADHD will experience academic difficulties as a result of their difficulties in sustaining attention, their being easily distracted, and the challenges they face with following directions. Because ADHD is considered a disability, children with this diagnosis can receive special help in school. Section 504 is a part of the US Rehabilitation Act of 1973 that prohibits discrimination based upon disability. Section 504 is a civil rights statute that requires that the needs of students with disabilities be met as adequately as the needs of the nondisabled are met. Examples of accommodations that children with ADHD may receive under a 504 plan include a structured learning environment, repeated or simplified instructions, modified testing procedures, use of tape recorders or calculators, and modified homework assignments. When children have comorbid ADHD and LDs they may be entitled to services under the US Individuals with Disabilities Education Act (IDEA). This federal law mandates that eligible students receive access to special education and/or related services, and that the services are designed to meet each child's unique educational needs. In this instance, clinicians should collaborate with the student, teachers, and parents to create an individualized education program (IEP). Types of accommodations or services that may be written into the IEP include special education services either within a self-contained classroom or within a resource setting (e.g., part-time special education services for specific academic areas).

> Children diagnosed with ADHD may be entitled to accommodations in school if the disorder impacts their learning

Children with ADHD are often referred to professionals because of a co-occurring disorder, including mood disorders, anxiety disorders, PTSD, obsessive-compulsive disorder, CD, or an SUD. If an adolescent is actively abusing substances, it is important to address the immediate addiction which may require physical treatments initially followed by ongoing psychotherapy for the substance abuse. After ADHD and potential comorbid disorders have been evaluated, providers should develop an intervention plan. Even though psychosocial interventions are frequently recommended complements to stimulant medication, psychopharmacological treatments are often the only treatments received by many individuals with ADHD due to the fact that many children and adolescents do not seek out or receive mental health services (Knopf, Park, & Mulye, 2008), and frequently mental health services are not available or accessible.

4

Treatment

4.1   Methods of Treatment

ADHD is a chronic neurodevelopmental disorder in which about 50% of children will continue to have the disorder in late adolescence (Wolraich et al., 2011), and 80% will retain at least some of the ADHD symptoms in adulthood (Barkley, Murphy, & Fischer, 2008). The chronic course of the disorder has several implications for treatment. First, clinicians should emphasize to families that ADHD is persistent across the lifespan, in most cases resulting in a need for long-term, coordinated care (Wolraich et al., 2011). Second, early intervention is critical for children with ADHD to help prevent and/or ameliorate the short- and long-term consequences of the disorder. Lastly, when implementing treatment plans, clinicians should take a long-term view. Even when treatment results in a reduction of the core symptoms of ADHD in the short-term, there may still be persistent associated problems (e.g., social challenges) or functional impairments (e.g., poor academic performance) that require continued intervention.

There are several well-established and evidence-based options for the treatment of children with ADHD that include pharmacological, psychosocial/behavioral therapies, psychoeducational interventions, and combined treatments. Because of the heterogeneity of ADHD symptoms and of the needs of those with the disorder, it is likely that various treatment plans will be appropriate for different children and their families. In addition, research suggests that specific therapies work best for ADHD when the disorder is comorbid with other particular psychiatric disorders (Jensen et al., 2001). In some cases, the treatments may actually be more effective for the comorbid disorder than for the ADHD. The child's age (preschool, elementary school, adolescence) should also be considered when selecting a treatment option. For example, behavioral therapy is recommended as a first-line treatment when working with preschoolers with ADHD (Wolraich et al., 2011). Finally, when choosing a treatment plan, it is often helpful for caregivers, teachers, and families to pinpoint specific behaviors and challenges to address. Once these goals are identified, it is easier to assess whether specific interventions are effective.

> Evidence-based treatments for ADHD include pharmacological, psychosocial/behavioral therapies, psychoeducation interventions, and combined treatments

4.2   Psychopharmacology

The most commonly prescribed psychotropic medications for the treatment of ADHD in school-aged children and adolescents is the class of agents known

Stimulants are the most common medication for treating children with ADHD

as stimulants (Zuvekas & Vitiello, 2012). The prescribing of stimulants has increased dramatically over the past 30 years. For example, from 2007 to 2010, prescriptions for stimulants within the past 30 days for children under 18 years of age were increased more than fivefold relative to those for the 6 years from 1988 to 1994 (Visser et al., 2014). Although stimulants are the most extensively researched psychotropics in the field of child and adolescent psychiatry (for a review, see Brown & Daly, 2009), controversy and public debate continue about the use of stimulant medication in the management of ADHD and whether stimulants are being overly prescribed for the disorder (LeFever, Arcona, & Antonuccio, 2003). Many explanations have been suggested for the increase in prescriptions, which include, but are not limited to, better identification of the disorder, less stigma than in previous years attached to medication as a treatment option, a recognition that there are specific subgroups of the disorder, and finally, the fact that there is poor access to mental health services, particularly among those individuals who have no insurance. Several factors found to be associated with medication treatment for ADHD include younger age, burden of impairment, and a recent health care contact (Visser, Lesesne, & Perou, 2007). The available evidence suggests that, in general, stimulants are not overprescribed to children and adolescents in the United States (Connor, 2011); however, there are certain geographic areas (e.g., western North Carolina) where stimulants are inappropriately or overly prescribed (Angold, Erkanli, Egger, & Costello, 2000).

Before the clinician discusses specific stimulant medications with children and their families, it is important to address the family's understanding and expectations regarding stimulants and their effects, and to provide psychoeducation about the benefits as well as the potential adverse side effects of these medications. With some of the newer stimulants (e.g., medications that are longer-acting and therefore require fewer doses), research has generally suggested that approximately 70–85% of children and adolescents respond to the stimulants (Pliszka & AACAP Work Group on Quality Issues, 2007). Stimulant medications have been demonstrated to improve some of the specific core symptoms associated with ADHD in the short-term. In particular, the stimulants are effective in enhancing attention and concentration while also reducing hyperactivity and impulsivity for children with ADHD (Barbaresi, Katusic, Colligan, Weaver, & Jacobsen, 2007). For example, research has demonstrated that individuals make fewer errors on vigilance tasks when treated with stimulant medication (i.e., methylphenidate; Quinlan, 2000). Research has also shown that stimulants decrease disruption in the classroom, increase academic productivity and on-task behavior, and improve teacher ratings of children's behavior (for a review, see Nigg & Barkley, 2014).

There are individual differences in response to medication

Families should be informed that there are also some major limitations of stimulant treatment. There are individual differences in response to medication, and not all children will positively respond to these medications. And, for those children who demonstrate a positive response, this rarely equates with a normalizing of their behavior (Nigg & Barkley, 2014). Interestingly, the stimulants have limited impact on domains of functional impairment associated with ADHD, including problems with social behavior and academic performance, which are frequently the primary reason that families seek treatment for their child (Nigg & Barkley, 2014). For example, although the stimulants appear to improve social functioning, these effects, albeit statistically significant, have not always been clinically significant (Tannock & Brown, 2000). Moreover, little research has demonstrated positive effects of the stimulants on academic achievement (Raggi & Chronis, 2006). Another significant limitation is that no long-term effects have been established for stimulant medication. There are also data that suggest that there is limited parent and/or teacher satisfaction with stimulant medication. In addition, there may be some preexisting family problems which are beyond the scope of medication. Other classes of psychotropics (e.g., specific serotonin reuptake inhibitors [SSRIs]) may prove more effective for ADHD when it is comorbid with anxiety disorder or depression. Finally, the stimulants may be contraindicated for some children and adolescents (e.g., in families where there is a member with an SUD).

Although the Food and Drug Administration (FDA) does not endorse the use of methylphenidate in children younger than 6 years, due to limited safety and efficacy data, there has been a substantial increase in the number of off-label prescriptions of stimulants for preschoolers (Zito et al., 2007). To provide a greater evidence base, the US NIMH funded a large-scale multisite clinical trial that systematically studied the safety and efficacy of immediate-release methylphenidate for preschool children 3 to 5 years of age (Greenhill et al., 2006). A notable limitation of the study was that it only included preschoolers who had moderate to severe dysfunction. Findings revealed that methylphenidate is safe and efficacious in preschool children. Recommendations include initiating treatment with lower doses because preschoolers metabolize stimulants at a slower rate relative to school-aged children, but then titrating upward in smaller doses (Greenhill et al., 2006). In addition, preschoolers experience more adverse side effects when treated with high doses of stimulants compared with school-aged children (Greenhill et al., 2006). It is noteworthy that stimulant medication for preschoolers is recommended as a second-line option and should only be considered for children with moderate to severe ADHD, when behavior therapy has not been effective, and when the symptoms have persisted for at least 9 months (Wolraich et al., 2011).

Practitioners should be cautious about prescribing stimulant medication for children under the age of 5

There is some research that has evaluated the effectiveness of stimulant medication for ADHD when there are comorbid diagnoses including mood disorders and anxiety disorders. The findings of these investigations are mixed; results from several studies suggested that responses to stimulant medications are compromised when comorbid conditions exist (Spencer, Wilens, Biederman, Wozniak, & Harding-Crawford, 2000; Tannock, Ickowicz, & Schachar, 1995). Alternatively, findings from two large-scale studies did not find an association between anxiety and stimulant response (Abikoff et al., 2005; MTA Cooperative Group, 1999). Two open trials (Findling, 1996; Gammon & Brown, 1993) suggest that combining SSRIs and stimulant medications is safe and effective; however, other reports caution that SSRIs are not effective for managing the symptoms associated with ADHD (Wilens, Spencer, & Biederman, 2000). Treatment recommendations from the Texas Children's Medication Algorithm Project (Pliszka et al., 2006) for comorbid ADHD and depression suggest treating the more serious disorder first. In the case of a positive symptom response for both disorders, the medication chosen for the more serious disorder is continued. If ADHD is treated first, and there is a positive response only to the ADHD symptoms, then an SSRI may be added for the purpose of treating the depression. If there is no response for either ADHD or depression, then the stimulant medication is stopped, and treatment for depression alone is considered. Use of a different ADHD medication is recommended if there is a positive response for the symptoms of depression, but not the symptoms of ADHD (Pliszka et al., 2006).

There is no evidence to suggest that stimulant use increases the chance of an individual developing problems with substance use or dependence. In fact, several studies found that the use of stimulant medication during childhood reduced the risk for substance abuse in adulthood (Barkley, Fischer, Smallish, & Fletcher, 2003; Biederman, Wilens, Mick, Spencer, & Faraone, 1999; Wilens et al., 2008). However, results from a recent meta-analysis indicated that stimulant medication used to treat childhood ADHD did not appear to increase or decrease the risk of later developing an SUD (Humphreys, Eng, & Lee, 2013). Because the stimulants have significant abuse potential, adolescents with ADHD should be assessed for substance abuse or diversion before being prescribed a stimulant medication. If the adolescent is abusing or suspected of abusing drugs, prescribing a nonstimulant medication for ADHD is recommended. Clinicians should actively monitor the response to medication in all children and adolescents, and should proceed with special care in the case of dual diagnoses, particularly substance abuse.

There are no explicit guidelines to help determine which stimulant medication to use first when treating a child with ADHD. It is more common in clinical practice for prescribers to use long-acting formulations instead of short-acting medications (Shier, Reichenbacher, Ghuman, & Ghuman, 2013). Children who do not observe benefits from one stimulant medication will often respond to another (for a review, see Brown & Daly, 2009), and response to one stimulant does not predict response to others. Some experts suggest that there is no clear empirical evidence for the use of methylphenidate over amphetamine or vice versa (Shier et al., 2013). However, a meta-analysis of 23 trials that compared various stimulant medications revealed that amphetamine-based formulations were moderately more efficacious than methylphenidate products (Faraone & Buitelaar, 2010). Another meta-analysis yielded similar effect sizes for immediate-release and long-acting stimulants for the treatment of ADHD, both of which were greater relative to the effect sizes for nonstimulant medications for the management of the ADHD disorder (Faraone, 2009).

All medication effects must be carefully monitored by clinicians. Brown (2000) noted that many children provide general descriptions of medication response, and advises that they need to receive instructions in reporting more specific reactions, particularly adverse effects. Treatment-emergent adverse side effects from stimulant medication may include decreased appetite, stomachache, insomnia, and headache (Barbaresi et al., 2006). Less common side effects include motor tics, headaches, nausea, fatigue, irritability, and increases in heart rate and blood pressure (Pliszka & AACAP Work Group on Quality Issues, 2007). Many side effects associated with the stimulants abate after a short period, or may disappear if the dosage or timing of administration is adjusted (Shier et al., 2013).

> **Special care is suggested when prescribing stimulant medication to young people with dual diagnoses**

> **Most prescribers suggest long-acting formulations instead of short-acting versions**

> **Use of stimulant medication must be carefully monitored for side effects**

4.2.1   Stimulant Medications

There are two groups of stimulant medications approved by the FDA for
the treatment of ADHD in children, each based on a different stimulant
compound: methylphenidate-based medications and amphetamine/dextro-
amphetamine-based medications. Methylphenidate has short-acting (Ritalin,
Methylin, Focalin), intermediate (Ritalin SR, Methylin ER, Metadate ER,
Metadate CD, Ritalin LA), and long-acting versions (Concerta, Focalin XR,
Daytrana patch, Quillivant XR). Similarly, amphetamine/dextroamphetamine
is available in short-acting (Dexedrine, Dextrostat), intermediate (Adderall,
Dexedrine Spansule), and long-acting formulas (Adderall XR, Vyvanse). Brief
descriptions of some of these specific drugs are given below (see Table 4).

Methylphenidate-
based medications
and amphetamine/
dextroamphetamine-
based medications
are approved by the
FDA

Table 4
FDA-Approved Medications for the Management of ADHD Symptoms

Class	Brand name	Short-acting	Long-acting	Common side effects
Stimulant medications				
Amphetamine/ dextroamphe- tamine	Adderall	✓		Loss of appetite, weight loss, sleep difficulties, irritability, tics.
	Adderall XR		✓	
	Dexedrine	✓		
	Dexedrine Spansule		✓	
	Dextrostat	✓		
	Vyvanse		✓	
Methyl- phenidate	Concerta		✓	Loss of appetite, weight loss, sleep difficulties, irritability, tics.
	Daytrana patch		✓	
	Focalin	✓		
	Focalin XR		✓	
	Metadate CD	Intermediate		
	Metadate ER	Intermediate		
	Methylin	✓		
	Methylin ER	Intermediate		
	Ritalin	✓		
	Ritalin LA	Intermediate		
	Ritalin SR	Intermediate		
	Quillivant XR		✓	
Nonstimulant medications				
Atomoxetine	Strattera		✓	Sleep difficulties, anxiety, fatigue, upset stomach, dizziness, dry mouth.
Guanfacine XR	Intuniv		✓	Sleepiness, headache, fatigue, abdominal pain.

The short-acting formula of methylphenidate (e.g., Ritalin, Methylin) is often administered twice a day, usually in the morning and early afternoon. The recommended starting dose of immediate-release methylphenidate is 5 mg, increasing in 5-mg increments up to 20 mg per dose. Ritalin can be consumed in 5-mg, 10-mg, or 20-mg tablets. Though the average dosage is 20 to 30 mg daily, there are children and adolescents who may need 40 to 60 mg, and others who will demonstrate symptom improvement on just 10 to 15 mg daily. Research has generally suggested that response to stimulant medication is independent of dose effects and is idiosyncratic across children (for a review, see Brown & Daly, 2009). Because immediate-release methylphenidate is fast-acting, the medication usually begins working about 15 to 30 min after ingestion, with beneficial effects being observed after 30 to 60 min, and peak effect occurring on the average of 90 to 120 min after it is taken, although this is frequently variable. For short-acting preparations, the effects can last from 2 to 4 hr. Although two doses per day is typical, the prescribing physician may decide in some cases that a third dose after school is warranted if the child continues to experience significant behavioral difficulties in the evening, or experiences a rebound effect. Because stimulants can wear off rapidly and leave the brain receptors too quickly, there may be a rebound effect whereby the child demonstrates increased irritability and aggression, emotional lability, and an exacerbation of the core symptoms of ADHD. The third dose of medication is usually half of the normal dose and is given about 30 min before the expected rebound symptoms for the purpose of easing the dissipation of the medication.

> Response to stimulant medication is independent of dose effects and is idiosyncratic across children

The intermediate-acting extended release tablets are usually taken once or twice a day. Ritalin SR is a sustained-release preparation tablet that initially releases 10 mg of methylphenidate, followed by an additional 10 mg approximately 4 hr later for a total duration of action of 8 hr. Since individuals metabolize medications differently, some children will derive greater benefit from two tablets, 4 hr apart, than one timed-release administration. The long-acting formulas are usually taken once a day, and effects can last from 8 to 12 hr. Concerta is a long-acting form of methylphenidate that was approved by the FDA in 2000, and is available in 18-mg, 27-mg, 36-mg, and 54-mg tablets. It uses a time-released system by means of an osmotic pump within the capsule to regulate consistent release of the medication throughout the course of the day. Another methylphenidate preparation, Metadate CD, delivers 30% of the dose immediately, and continually releases the remainder of the medication throughout the day.

Dextroamphetamine is prepared in several different ways. The short-acting version (Dexedrine) is in tablet form of 5 mg and 10 mg, and on average one to three tablets are provided for each dose every 4 to 5 hr. Dexedrine Spansule is available in 5 mg, 10 mg, and 15 mg, and usually have an effect that lasts for about 6 to 8 hr. Dexedrine Spansule may take up to 1 hr to be effective. Other variants of dextroamphetamine include amphetamine salt tablets (Adderall) that usually last about 6 hr and are given once or twice a day depending on the length of therapeutic effect. Adderall XR is the longer acting amphetamine preparation and provides control of ADHD symptoms for up to 12 hr. Vyvanse is considered a *prodrug* because it is inactive until metabolized in the body. The mechanism of action is thought to help prevent abuse of the drug, which has been found to occur with Adderall.

Several stimulant preparations have been developed for those cases in which the oral forms are not well tolerated, when the child has difficulty with pill swallowing, or when there are issues of compliance. In 2006, the FDA approved a methylphenidate patch, Daytrana, to be used as an alternative to orally administered medications. The patch is attached to the individual's skin near the hip and can be worn for up to 9 hr daily. For children who have trouble swallowing pills, Focalin is a stimulant that comes in a capsule, and can be opened and sprinkled on foods

Individual responses to stimulant medication are quite variable, and health professionals should collaborate with children and adolescents and their caregivers to carefully evaluate the child's response to medication. Stimulants should be carefully and gradually titrated so that an optimal dose is reached – that is, one that manages specific target behaviors (e.g., teacher ratings of inattention) while still resulting in the fewest adverse side effects. The dose is at an appropriate level when maximum benefits can be observed, and adverse side effects are at a minimum. During the titration period, the medication should be used for 7 days, so that changes can be observed across a range of settings. During this period, children and family members should attempt to observe the effects of medication over the course of each day, and compare these observations with the structure of environmental demands. It is especially useful to note the times of day where the effects of medication begin to dissipate, and to attempt to have these times correspond to recreation or mealtimes or other situations where high levels of concentration are not required. In addition, ingesting stimulants with meals or snacks can help alleviate some common adverse side effects, such as gastrointestinal inflammation.

> Children's response to medication should be carefully monitored

4.2.2   Nonstimulant Medications

Atomoxetine (Strattera) is a nonstimulant medication approved by the FDA in 2002 that has been used for the management of ADHD. It is in a class of drugs called norepinephrine reuptake inhibitors because they affect the transmitters of norepinephrine, a natural substance in the brain that helps manage behavior. Atomoxetine is not classified as a stimulant, although it does have some stimulant effects. It is not a drug that is abused by users, and prescriptions for the drug can be written without Schedule II restrictions because it is not classified as a stimulant medication. Atomoxetine is usually taken either once or twice daily. It lasts for 24 hr and therefore provides a therapeutic effect that lasts throughout the day and night. In contrast to the stimulants, dosing for atomoxetine is based on weight, and full therapeutic effect may not be achieved until the child has taken it for 3 to 4 weeks.

> Several nonstimulant medications have been approved by the FDA for the treatment of ADHD

Another recent psychotropic therapy for ADHD is modafinil (Provigil), which is a cognitive enhancement agent primarily used to promote wakefulness. Modafinil differs structurally from other drugs for ADHD, and selectively targets the cerebral cortex (Biederman et al., 2005). It has been prescribed as an off-label treatment for ADHD (Rugino & Samsock, 2003). Modafinil is usually administered once daily, with dose levels of approximately 170 to 425 mg.

Clonidine (Catapres, Nexicon) and guanfacine (Tenex) are α-adrenergic agonists that also come in FDA-approved long-acting 24-hr release versions

(Kapvay and Intuniv). Clonidine comes in tablet or patch form and is most effective in reducing hyperactive and aggressive behaviors, with less improvement demonstrated for problems with focusing or sustaining attention (Ming, Mulvey, Mohanty, & Patel, 2011). It is usually administered in the evening before bedtime to help children sleep.

For children with comorbid diagnoses, particularly comorbidity of the internalizing disorders (e.g., anxiety disorders or depression), other psychotropic medications that target depression, anxiety, or mood lability may be prescribed. Children may be prescribed tricyclic antidepressants (TCAs), including imipramine (Tofranil), nortriptyline (Pamelor) and desipramine (Norpramin). Other physicians prescribe bupropion (Wellbutrin) or clonidine (Catapres).

Collaboration is important when making treatment decisions about medication

For children with ADHD, medication decisions should be reached through collaboration between caregivers, teachers, and medical personnel. Before a child begins a medication regimen, he or she should undergo a physical evaluation that assesses height, weight, pulse, and blood pressure to determine whether there are any preexisting medical conditions. When children begin taking medications for ADHD, they should begin with a low dose of the drug (typically 5 mg for the immediate-release formulations; starting doses are more variable for the intermediate and long-acting formulations), and gradually increase the dose. It is recommended that prescribing physicians monitor medication effects weekly during the titration period, and monthly once medication doses are established. Based on each child's specific response to the medication, caregivers and health professionals can determine the dose that is best suited to the child for the specific target symptoms to be addressed. In the weeks and months following the commencement of drug treatment, children and adolescents should monitor and evaluate ADHD symptoms and adverse side effects, in collaboration with families, teachers and clinicians. Measures to assess the child's response to medication should be similar to those assessments used to diagnose and identify specific target behaviors for which the medication may be intended.

Drug holidays are recommended to evaluate the need for medication and to reduce side effects

Some families and children's physicians choose to provide the child with a structured treatment interruption, also called a *drug holiday.* Drug holidays are most frequently taken during the summer months, but may also occur on weekends or during vacations. There are several potential advantages to a drug holiday. First, the drug holiday provides the opportunity for caregivers and practitioners to again obtain a baseline of behavior without medication to determine if the medication – or the same dosage – is needed. This information is useful when deciding whether to readminister the medication at the beginning of the school year. Second, children who experience adverse side effects such as appetite suppression or insomnia as a result of the medication are able to spend some extended time without active medication. Alternatively, drug holidays are contraindicated if children and families are in the midst of stressful circumstances, or if the absence of active medication could actually precipitate dangers such as accidents or abuse (Weiss, Hechtman, & Weiss, 1999).

It is important that the child's privacy and confidentiality be protected when children require the administration of ADHD medications during school hours. Medication management should include careful monitoring and follow-up attention by medical doctors, psychologists, teachers, and family members to address untoward side effects and the effect of the medication on ADHD symptoms. Frequently, multiple dosing of medication during the school hours is difficult, and many children and especially adolescents find this to be stigmatizing. Hence those preparations of stimulants that are made for longer duration of action may be most appropriate for these children and adolescents.

4.3   Psychosocial/Behavioral Therapies

Although there is a compelling evidence base for medication for the treatment of ADHD, caregivers frequently rate the option of medication lower in acceptability compared with nonmedical treatments (Fiks et al., 2012). There are several forms of psychosocial and behavioral treatments that may be useful for children with ADHD. Because many young people with ADHD also have other psychological symptoms that may include depression or aggression, therapy can address aspects of functioning that may not necessarily be responsive to pharmacotherapy. Psychosocial therapies can also target issues common to children with ADHD, such as low self-esteem and self-efficacy. Many young people with ADHD, especially those who did not receive early intervention, have had to endure others' assessments of them as "lazy, ineffective, unfocused, or poorly behaved." Others may have recognized the child's functional deficits and attributed these impairments to inherent characteristics rather than a neurodevelopmental disorder. Since children and adolescents affected by ADHD have often internalized these negative messages, thereby impacting self-esteem, psychological interventions can help target and correct these inaccurate judgments and their effects on self-schemas.

> Psychosocial and behavioral treatments may be useful for young people with ADHD

Family therapy is often a helpful intervention for children with ADHD. Therapists should emphasize that many behaviors demonstrated by children with ADHD stem from the disorder. Caregivers are a critical part of the support and encouragement that is necessary for children to develop self-esteem and effective methods for coping with ADHD. At the same time, every child is different, and not every behavior is attributable to ADHD. Furthermore, caregivers are likely to have additional issues to bring to therapy besides their child's ADHD. These factors affect their child's experience and the family's management of ADHD. There are a number of strategic family approaches available that include behavior management within the context of a family systems approach (for a review, see Barkley, 2006).

Behavioral techniques are commonly used for individuals with ADHD and have been demonstrated as the psychotherapy of choice for the disorder because of their well-established evidence base in the extant literature. Behavioral interventions are based on the principles of social learning theory and contingency management. Behavior therapy may be helpful in its emphasis on structure and its reinforcement of positive behaviors. Behavior therapy can include interventions that are taught to caregivers and teachers. Children may demonstrate the greatest degree of behavior change when they receive consistent responses for their actions and behavior. Methods of behavior therapy may include management skills for caregivers and teachers, contingency management approaches (such as time-outs and positive reinforce-

> Behavioral techniques that reinforce positive behavior, applied in the classroom or at home, have been found to be very effective in the treatment of ADHD

ment), self-management strategies for the child (e.g., self-monitoring and self-reinforcement), and training that targets social skills and problem solving. For the child and caregiver, consistency and follow-up are important components of successful treatment with behavior therapy. For the practitioner, behavioral interventions require customization and ongoing efforts to monitor and maintain. For a review of behavioral techniques that may be helpful for children with ADHD, the interested reader is referred to Reiff and Tippins (2004).

Over the past 4 decades, numerous studies have demonstrated that behavioral interventions in the home and school setting are effective (albeit with moderate effect sizes) and associated with reductions of symptoms and functional impairments related to ADHD (Evans, Owens, & Bunford, 2014). In fact, it has been suggested that the effects of tightly controlled behavior management are equivalent to low to moderate doses of stimulant medication (for a review, see Pelham & Waschbusch, 1999). By contrast to studies of stimulant medication, studies of behavioral treatments have focused on functional impairments associated with ADHD. These effects are believed to mediate the long-term outcomes associated with ADHD, including parenting practices, peer relationships, and school functioning (for a review, see APA Working Group on Psychoactive Medications for Children and Adolescents, 2006). Well-established behavioral treatments for ADHD include behavioral parent training, behavioral peer interventions, behavioral classroom management, and organization skills training (Evans et al., 2014). Additional treatment modalities that have been researched but have not yet met the criteria necessary for classification as well-established treatments include combining training programs – for example, medication and behavioral therapy (probably efficacious), neurofeedback training (possibly efficacious), and cognitive training (experimental treatment; Evans et al., 2014).

Behavioral treatments are described in more detail in the sections below. However, there are several important considerations for the clinician when delivering behavioral interventions. First, the clinician needs to consider and address cross-situational impairments for the child with ADHD. Therefore, treatments should be implemented in all settings (e.g., home, school, situations involving peers) in which the child demonstrates some impairment. This is especially important because of the challenge of poor generalizability of treatment from the office setting to real-world settings. Second, children with ADHD often struggle in the school setting with behavior and academic performance. Therefore, academic interventions are frequently needed in addition to behavioral interventions (Raggi & Chronis, 2006). Third, for behavioral treatments to be successful, environmental contingencies must be delivered consistently. Maintaining treatment fidelity and consistency of treatment are often challenging when working with children with ADHD. Finally, clinicians should be aware that parental psychopathology can interfere with implementation.

4.3.1 Behavioral Parent Training

A number of studies have examined behavioral parent training (BPT), including for compliance with parental requests, rule following, and defiant and aggressive behavior, as well as symptoms associated with ADHD (for a review, see Nigg & Barkley, 2014). The behaviors associated with ADHD may negatively impact the parent–child relationship, as well as increase caregiver stress and burden (Wells et al., 2006). Caregivers of children with ADHD may feel overwhelmed in trying to manage their child's behavior, which in turn may further compromise their coping ability as well as their use of appropriate parenting strategies. Consequently, some caregivers may engage in a pattern of responding to their child's behavior that either maintains or further exacerbates the behavioral difficulties. Therefore, the primary goal of BPT is to assist caregivers in modifying the antecedents and consequences of their child's behavior to promote more socially acceptable behavior.

> The goal of parent training is to modify antecedents and consequences of the child's behavior

Contingency management approaches used in BPT emphasize behavior modification, cues and consequences, reward systems, and discipline (Chronis, Chacko, Fabiano, Wymbs, & Pelham, 2004). Common strategies employed within a behavioral framework for children with ADHD include (1) psychoeducation about ADHD, (2) providing structure and adhering to routines, (3) setting clear rules and expectations, (4) giving effective commands and instructions, (5) delivering contingent attention and praise, (6) planned ignoring, (7) use of a point system or token economy, (8) time-out and loss of privileges and response cost, (9) daily school-home report card, (10) cueing (conducting activities in a consistent place each day – e.g., doing homework at the same desk each day), and (11) attending an intensive summer treatment program.

Successful interventions that involve caregivers emphasize the need for structure and routine in children's lives. Caregivers of children with ADHD are instructed on how to set limits and respond consistently to undesirable behaviors with specific, brief, and clear commands and instructions. Training within a behavioral context is focused on educating caregivers about developmentally appropriate behaviors and responding only to behaviors that are within the child's control (McMahon & Forehand, 2003). Contingent attention and praise is used to positively reinforce appropriate behaviors demonstrated by the child, while planned ignoring (extinction) is used for minor problematic behaviors to reduce or eliminate them. Positive attention delivered immediately following an appropriate behavior serves to increase the likelihood of that behavior in the future (Eiraldi, Mautone, & Power, 2012).

A token economy is a point system for providing positive reinforcement to a child by giving the child tokens (e.g., stickers, check marks, marbles) for completing tasks or behaving in desired ways. Importantly, the desired behaviors should be predetermined and should be very specific (e.g., sitting at the dinner table for 5 min). Once the child has earned the requisite number of tokens by engaging in the target behavior, he or she can exchange these tokens for small prizes or rewards. This system works best when the there is a menu of reward items for the child to choose from and when the caregivers are consistent with their adherence to and implementation of the program.

> A token economy can be used to positively reinforce appropriate behaviors

A time-out is a negative punishment procedure whereby the time-out serves as the loss of access to positive reinforcement for a brief period, in response to the child's engaging in a problem behavior. A response cost is when the child loses a specific amount of reinforcement. Appropriate discipline needs to be consistent, and concrete rewards and consequences need to be the standard in caregivers' management of the ADHD child's behavior. Caregivers need to avoid ineffective discipline techniques, such as administering punishment without advance warning or without the child's having understood that their behavior had resulted in those consequences.

4.3.2   Behavioral Peer Interventions

Behavioral peer interventions can augment school- and home-based interventions

Behavioral peer interventions are another treatment that may be useful for children who have ADHD. These interventions focus on teaching social skills and social problem solving, enhancing behavioral competencies, and decreasing aggression as well as other undesirable social behaviors (e.g., controlling behavior, bullying). Inattention and hyperactivity can preclude children from forming appropriate relationships with their peers, learning to listen, taking turns, and controlling impulses that can facilitate the development of healthy friendships. Most children are not apt to accept their peers who impulsively blurt out things in the classroom or who intrude on others' activities. Children with ADHD may be described as annoying, bossy, immature, boastful, intrusive, and overbearing (Pelham, Fabiano, Gnagy, et al., 2005). Therefore, instruction provided in behavioral peer interventions is designed to promote cooperation, communication, and participation. Enhancing the social skills of children with ADHD is important, given that children with ADHD exhibit significantly more problems with peer relationships when compared with those without the disorder (Nangle & Erdley, 2001) and experience more peer rejection (Hoza et al., 2005). Consistent with the chronic nature of ADHD, deficits in peer relationships and social functioning have been shown to continue well into adolescence and even adulthood (e.g., Barkley, Fischer, Smallish, & Fletcher, 2004).

There is some evidence that a heavy focus on social skills deficits may improve social functioning in children with ADHD (Gol & Jarus, 2005) and hopefully peer relationships as well. However, positive effects from this training are only evident when it is part of a more intensive multimodal behavioral treatment package that is delivered within the child's social milieu (Pelham, Fabiano, Gnagy, et al., 2005). Therefore, behavioral peer interventions are frequently delivered in school-based social skills groups, weekend groups, and summer camp programs (Pelham, Fabiano, Gnagy, et al., 2005). In addition, these programs are used simultaneously with parent training, school-based interventions, or their combination. Findings from the MTA that involved a combination of parent training, teacher consultation, and a summer camp program that focused on peer interventions revealed large pretest to posttest improvements in behavioral functioning, social skills, and peer relations that were actually sustained at the 2-year follow-up assessment. Strategies employed during the summer camp program included social skills training, coached recreational activities, and contingency behavior management systems that reinforced desirable social behaviors (Pelham, Fabiano, Gnagy, et al., 2005).

4.3.3   Behavioral Classroom Management

Managing children with ADHD is often challenging for teachers. ADHD symptoms can affect attention, comprehension, assignment completion, and group dynamics within the classroom setting. The frustration students experience as a result of ADHD may be associated with additional behavior problems such as aggression, emotional lability, or tantrums. Fortunately, there is compelling evidence attesting to the efficacy of behavioral approaches in the classroom setting (for a review, see Daly, Creed, Xanthopoulos, & Brown, 2007). Teachers utilize many of the same previously described behavioral modification strategies such as contingency management and token and point systems. A behavioral intervention with strong research support that is frequently used in the classroom setting is the Daily Report Card (DRC; Fabiano et al., 2010). The DRC is an approach that entails collaboration among the child with ADHD, the caregivers, and the teacher in selecting two to three clearly defined positive behavioral goals. Common target behaviors in the classroom that receive attention include completing assigned classroom work, obeying classroom rules, on-task behavior, complying with teacher requests, and getting along with other classmates. Teachers are responsible for monitoring and recording the student's success in meeting the behavioral goals. The DRC is sent home each school day and provides feedback to the child and caregiver about the child's goal attainment for that particular day or week. The caregiver is then responsible for administering the reinforcer (e.g., a small prize) if the child achieved the goal for the day or the week.

> **Behavioral approaches have proven to be very effective in the classroom setting**

In addition to the DRC, teachers may benefit from introducing the most difficult material at the beginning of the day, by clarifying the steps needed to complete tasks, minimizing multitasking requirements, varying methods of instruction, and alleviating potentially distracting elements from the students' classroom environments. Teachers can also maximize the effectiveness of interactions with students with ADHD by giving clear and concise instructions, maintaining eye contact with the student, remaining calm, and establishing and following clear and consistent classroom rules. Teachers should endeavor to respond with sensitivity and cultivate self-esteem in individuals with ADHD. Rewards are likely to be more effective than reprimands and punishments, and teachers can assist in identifying methods of encouraging each student in negotiating many of the challenges associated with ADHD.

4.3.4 Academic Interventions and Organizational Skills Training

Academic interventions target the academic performance of children with ADHD by focusing on target behaviors (e.g., seat-work productivity) as well as academic instruction, materials, or the environment. Teachers may use a contingency management approach to strategy training with the goal of improving target behaviors such as note-taking skills (e.g., increased detail, increased independence) and on-task behavior (for a review, see Langberg, Epstein, & Graham, 2008). Caregivers also can influence children's success at school by helping children with strategies to record and complete homework assignments, keep school papers in appropriate folders or binders, and setting specific times for homework assignments and studying times. In other situations, caregivers can have children repeat-back instructions that are especially

> **Teachers can use a contingency management approach to improve note-taking skills and on-task behaviors**

important to ensure comprehension of the assignment (for a review, see Raggi & Chronis, 2006).

The literature examining the efficacy of computer-assisted instruction (CAI) for academic skills is limited, although there is preliminary support for the use of CAI in increasing academic achievement across multiple areas of performance such as mathematics (Mautone, DuPaul, & Jitendra, 2005; Ota & DuPaul, 2002), science (Shaw & Lewis, 2005), oral reading fluency (Clarfield & Stoner, 2005), and attention and concentration (Navarro et al., 2003).

4.3.5   School Accommodations

Caregivers and teachers should be aware of the Individuals with Disabilities Education Act (IDEA) and Section 504 of the Rehabilitation Act of 1973

It is important that families and teachers are aware of the federal mandates that ensure the rights of children with ADHD in the United States who demonstrate eligibility for special services and accommodations under legislation. These include the US IDEA and the US Rehabilitation Act of 1973 (Section 504). School districts are required to offer "free appropriate public education" to eligible children who may qualify for these services due to the fact that they have a specific disability. Many children with ADHD may not meet criteria for services under the IDEA, but may be protected under Section 504. Children whose ADHD does not affect their learning processes may not be considered eligible for services under the IDEA or Section 504.

Under the IDEA, ADHD may be viewed as pertaining to the category of "Other Health Impairment" (OHI) if the disorder manifests itself through impairments in vitality, strength, or alertness. The IDEA requires every school district to obtain a complete evaluation for each child who may be eligible for special education and related programs. After the evaluation, the child's IEP team considers the information from the evaluation for the purpose of creating a plan that addresses the educational needs of the child. An ADHD diagnosis in and of itself does not necessarily indicate that a child is eligible for special education services or other programs. Children with ADHD may also meet requirements under other disability categories of IDEA, such as "Specific Learning Disability" or "Emotional Disturbance," if the individuals have comorbid diagnoses (e.g., ADHD and a psychiatric diagnosis, ADHD and an LD).

If a child is eligible for services under the IDEA, teachers, mental health professionals, and caregivers create an IEP that includes specific goals that are assessed each year. These goals may include standards for academic achievement, emotional functioning, and specific behavioral objectives. Caregivers participate in developing the IEP, and the plan cannot be changed without their input. Every child who receives services through IDEA must have an IEP. Students with ADHD who obtain services through Section 504 are provided with programs created to address their specific challenges and needs. Children who are deemed eligible for Section 504 must demonstrate that the disorder requires specialized programs or educational formats. Such modifications may consist of curriculum changes, different classroom organizations, tailored teaching techniques and instructions for homework and studying, use of behavior management techniques, and increased dialogue between caregivers and teachers.

4.3.6 Neurofeedback Training

Neurofeedback training seeks to improve cognitive deficits in children with ADHD by providing feedback from brain waves as measured by EEG. There have been few randomized clinical trials conducted that systematically examined the effectiveness of neurofeedback training in young people with ADHD. One recent study compared neurofeedback training with computerized attention training in children with ADHD between the ages of 8 and 12 years (Gevensleben et al., 2009). Findings revealed parent-and teacher-rated improvements of ADHD symptoms for the children receiving neurofeedback training. However, no group differences were noted on measures of important functional behaviors in social, academic, or home functioning.

4.3.7 Cognitive Training

Cognitive enhancement training utilizing computers is a relatively new treatment modality for children and adolescents with ADHD. The computerized training targets improvements in working memory and attention through practice and immediate performance feedback (Sibley, Kuriyan, Evans, Waxmonsky, & Smith, 2014). The intervention takes the form of a software program that children use over the course of several weeks (Sinha, 2005). To date, two randomized trials have been conducted with children with ADHD; however, the results of both were equivocal. A study conducted by Beck and colleagues (2010) found significant benefits for the intervention group on ADHD symptoms and behaviors as rated by parents; however, few positive effects for these same outcomes were noted by teachers. Another study of cognitive training conducted by van der Oord and colleagues (2014) also found improvements on parent ratings of ADHD symptoms and behaviors for the intervention group relative to the waitlist control group. Consistent with the findings of the Beck et al. (2010) intervention, no differences were found for teacher ratings of behaviors.

Cognitive enhancement training seeks to improve working memory and attention

4.3.8 Psychoeducation

Regardless of whether the treatment plan focuses on medication management, psychosocial/behavioral intervention, or a combination of therapies, practitioners are encouraged to provide psychoeducation to the child and their caregivers. Psychoeducational components are often a key element in successful treatment, and clients, caregivers, or family members may need to be trained in the most effective ways to advocate for those with ADHD. Interventions can include special accommodations for students with ADHD, such as classroom formats with increased variation and interaction, additional time for completion of tests and papers, tutoring, and instruction regarding specific note-taking and study techniques. In addition to the use of psychotherapy or medication, many health care professionals may refer their patients to helpful books, videotapes, or Internet sites that provide accessible information regarding the etiology and management of ADHD. A number of these sources are listed in the Appendix.

Some children with ADHD or their caregivers may find it helpful to join self-help or support groups. Children and Adults with Attention-Deficit/Hyperactivity Disorder (CHADD) and the National Attention Deficit Disorder Association both provide information, support, and resources for individuals and families affected by ADHD. These groups are often helpful in providing current information about ADHD, and also offer the benefits of a support network that may assist individuals and their families to cope with the disorder and become effective advocates either for themselves or their family members.

4.4   Variations and Combinations of Methods

Combined treatment techniques are especially effective for children with comorbid disorders or a negative long-term prognosis

The gold standard in the management of ADHD comprises at least two essential components: medication and psychotherapeutic interventions, particularly behavioral, with children and their caregivers (Wolraich et al., 2011). Research suggests that multimodal treatment is moderately superior to pharmacological or nonpharmacological interventions employed alone (Brown et al., 2005; Pelham, Burrows-Maclean, et al., 2005; Sibley et al., 2014). For instance, the NIMH's MTA was the largest and most comprehensive clinical trial of ADHD treatment outcomes to date (MTA Cooperative Group, 1999). In this collaborative, multisite study, 579 children between the ages of 7 and 10 years with combined subtype ADHD were assigned randomly to one of four treatment groups: state-of-the-art medication management, intensive behavioral intervention, medication and behavioral interventions combined, and a community treatment control group that received routine standard care (usually medication). While all four groups improved over time, the medication management and combined intervention groups demonstrated significantly greater improvements in core ADHD symptoms relative to the behavioral treatment alone and the community care group. However, only children in the combined group exhibited consistently significant better outcomes than those in the community care group across other important functional domains (e.g., disruptive behavior, parent–child relations, social skills, academic achievement). Furthermore, the results for the combined treatment group were demonstrated to be superior to those for medication alone in children with comorbid conditions (e.g., anxiety). Children who received multimodal treatment required lower stimulant doses than those treated with medication alone, and parents report being most satisfied with the behavioral and combined treatment approaches. After aggregating a broad array of symptom and functional domains into an omnibus composite outcome measure, children who received the combined intervention demonstrated the best treatment response. Based on these findings, multimodal treatments are recommended as the treatment of choice for children with ADHD.

Although findings from the 14-month MTA provide compelling evidence for the short-term efficacy of multimodal treatments, a recent follow-up investigation suggested that the type of ADHD treatment does not predict functioning 6 to 8 years later (Molina et al., 2009). In nearly all of the analyses that were conducted, the original randomized treatment groups did not differ on repeated assessments or recently clinically relevant variables that were obtained at the follow-up assessment (e.g., school grades, arrests, psychiatric hospitalizations). Medication use decreased by 62% after completion of the study, although statistically controlling for this finding did not alter results. Children still treated with medication 6 and 8 years after the commencement of the controlled trial (by community practitioners) fared no better than those who discontinued medication, despite the 41% increase in average daily dosages as well as the advent of improved long-acting stimulants during the follow-up period. These findings suggest that while medication and multi-modal treatments produce marked acute reductions of symptoms and impairment, these differential effects attenuate when treatment becomes less intense or ceases.

Findings from the MTA follow-up study also underscore the importance of initial clinical presentation, including severity of ADHD symptoms, comorbidity, conduct problems, intellectual functioning, and sociodemographic variables, for the long-term prognosis of the disorder. Regardless of treatment type, early ADHD symptom trajectory (i.e., within the first 3 years) predicted over one half (55%) of the clinical outcomes for those who originally participated in the study. Additionally, strength of ADHD symptom response to any treatment emerged as a predictor of later adolescent functioning. These findings document the suggestion that children with behavioral and sociodemographic advantages and those who respond favorably to any treatment modality tend to show the most favorable long-term prognosis (Molina et al., 2009).

A follow-up investigation also compared participants in the MTA group with a local comparison group of children without ADHD. While children in the MTA maintained functional improvements relative to baseline (pretreatment), they nevertheless demonstrated poorer outcomes than children without ADHD on the vast majority (91%) of dependent variables examined. For instance, children in the MTA investigation exhibited substantially higher ratings of overactivity and impulsivity and lower standardized test scores and academic performance than their peers without ADHD. ADHD children in the MTA group also had higher rates of grade retention, delinquency, arrest, and psychiatric hospitalization than their non-ADHD counterparts. Hence, despite substantial improvements after receiving intensive multimodal ADHD treatment, children continue to exhibit significant impairment across multiple domains during adolescence as compared with their non-ADHD peers (Molina et al., 2009). Thus, adequate management of ADHD does not restore these children to normality.

Taken together, findings from the MTA and other controlled clinical trials call attention to the need for effective ADHD treatments that can be feasibly maintained through childhood and adolescence. There is some evidence to suggest that combination or multimodal treatment is *less* cost-effective than medication management employed alone for treating core ADHD symptoms (Jensen et al., 2005). Clearly, multimodal treatment is a time-intensive venture that necessitates the involvement of multiple professionals. Nonetheless, Jensen and colleagues (2005) also note that combined treatment may be *more* cost-effective for some children with comorbid psychiatric disorders (e.g., anxiety, depression) than medication management employed alone. Moreover, because combined approaches generally produce improvements with lower doses of medication, the risk to benefit ratio of multimodal therapies may be

It is important that ADHD treatments are maintained through childhood and adolescence whenever feasible

more favorable than higher doses of stimulant medication employed alone, which can result in untoward side effects.

Beyond feasibility and cost-effectiveness, other important issues regarding effective treatment of ADHD remain to be addressed. In particular, clinicians are often faced with difficult decisions as to whether medication alone or multimodal therapy should be employed as a first-line treatment, how specific components of treatment should be sequenced, and the appropriate duration and intensity of interventions. While additional research is needed to provide clearer guidelines, initial evidence suggests that medication should be implemented as a first-line treatment for children with favorable clinical presentations (e.g., less severe symptoms and impairment), while multimodal approaches may be most appropriate for those who are at greater risk for a poorer long-term or guarded prognosis (i.e., these ADHD children with more severe symptoms and impairment, comorbid conditions, sociodemographic disadvantages).

4.5   Mechanisms of Action

Most research evidence suggests deficiencies in the reuptake of neurotransmitters at the synapses, particularly in levels of dopamine and norepinephrine among children with ADHD relative to comparison children, although epinephrine and serotonin have also been implicated (Nigg & Barkley, 2014).

Stimulant medications produce their effects through the neurotransmitters or various chemicals in the brain

The stimulants produce their effects through the neurotransmitters or various chemicals through which the neurons of the brain communicate with each other. Specifically, it is hypothesized that the stimulants work by increasing norepinephrine and dopamine actions by blocking their reuptake at the synapses and thereby facilitating the various neurotransmitters' (norepinephrine, dopamine) release. The neurotransmitters are exposed to enzymes that metabolize them. This leads to enhancement of extracellular dopamine and norepinephrine activity at the synaptic level of the central nervous system, especially in the prefrontal cortex and basal ganglia regions of the brain (for a review, see Brown & Daly, 2009). Stimulant medication increases neurotransmitter activity thereby reducing behavioral inhibition as well as enhancing attention and concentration, self-regulation, and executive functions (Nigg & Barkley, 2014).

The various stimulants exert disparate effects on neurochemical processes (Solanto, Arnsten, & Castellanos, 2001). For example, it is likely that methylphenidate blocks the dopamine transporter within the synaptic cleft, which in turn increases the release of dopamine. This process enhances attention, focus, and concentration in individuals who have impaired dopaminergic signals, a hypothesized deficit among individuals with ADHD. Positron emission tomography (PET) techniques demonstrate that therapeutic levels of methylphenidate block over half of the brain's dopamine transporters and increase the concentration of dopamine in the basal ganglia (Volkow, Fowler, Wang, Ding, & Gatley, 2002). Amphetamine, a stimulant similar to methylphenidate, exerts its therapeutic effect by elevating extracellular dopamine; however, it prolongs dopamine receptor signaling in the striatum (Calipari & Ferris, 2013).

The mechanism of action for the nonstimulants has some similarities and differences when compared with those of the stimulant formulations. For example, although atomoxetine inhibits presynaptic norepinephrine reuptake, thereby increasing extracellular norepinephrine, the increase in dopamine in the prefrontal cortex is more indirect (Nigg & Barkley, 2014; Wilens, 2006). In addition, atomoxetine exerts little effect on serotonin and other neurotransmitters. The therapeutic benefit of atomoxetine is believed to occur through its influence on the posterior attentional systems (Wilens, 2006). Guanfacine XR (extended release), one of a class of drugs termed the α-adrenergics, which also is antihypertensive, has a very different mechanism of action whereby the medication fine-tunes the α-2 receptions on nerve cells in the prefrontal cortex thereby producing enhanced signal strength and conductivity (Nigg & Barkley, 2014). It is believed that the therapeutic effects of the α-adrenergics on the prefrontal cortex result in improved neuropsychological functioning in young people with ADHD (Wilens, 2006).

While the stimulants do exert some effect on impulsivity and hyperactivity, in reality the effect of the stimulants in these two areas is the least understood. The effects of stimulants on social skills are equivocal. Though the literature generally suggests that children experience enhanced attention and concentration and less peer provocation while on stimulant medication, there is no evidence that children with ADHD are actually more likeable or are rated as more socially desirable while receiving stimulant medication.

The stimulants are effective in enhancing attention and concentration

Psychotherapy is likely to effect change in a multitude of ways. Structured forms of psychotherapy for some older children and adolescents may assist persons with ADHD in forming goals, identifying obstacles to accomplishing such goals, and meeting challenges in ways that can be applied to everyday situations. In addition, psychoeducation for ADHD may enable children and families to gain a better understanding of this life-long disorder, and assist them in making more informed treatment decisions.

Behavioral interventions are based on principles of social learning theory and contingency management. Therefore, the goal of behavior therapy is to offer children and their caregivers specific tools and avenues with which they can address the behavioral difficulties they experience that are related to ADHD. When children, their caregivers, and the clinician agree on those strategies to incorporate for the purpose of coping with the disorder, these may be practiced both within and outside of therapy sessions. Such strategies may include list making, creating specific times set aside for organization of tasks, and assessments of plans and priorities. If the chosen actions prove effective, children may learn new methods and ways of living that can replace old patterns and habits. The same principles are relevant for caregivers of children with ADHD whose parenting is apt to be affected by the disorder. Learning new and effective parenting techniques demands an initial investment of time and practice; however, new methods are eventually learned, and can become automatic, thereby producing consistent and effective responses that deter undesirable behaviors and promote positive actions. Thus, changes in parenting practices are conceptualized as the mechanism of action by which parent training influences the behavior of children and adolescents with ADHD (Weersing & Weisz, 2002).

4.6   Treating Children With ADHD and Comorbid Conditions

Few controlled trials have compared the efficacy of interventions for ADHD children with and without comorbid conditions. With regard to co-occurring anxiety disorders, there is emerging evidence to suggest the efficacy of both pharmacological and behavioral treatments (Antshel et al., 2011). Findings from one study suggested that comorbid anxiety does not impact stimulant efficacy (Garcia et al., 2009), and there is some evidence to suggest that children with ADHD treated with stimulants are less likely to develop other psychiatric comorbidities during adolescence (Biederman, Monuteaux, Spencer, Wilens, & Faraone, 2009; Wilens et al., 2008). Using data from the MTA, Jensen and colleagues (2001) found that children with ADHD and co-occurring anxiety disorders responded equally well to the behavioral and medication interventions relative to those with ADHD alone who responded best to the combined intervention. Further, Geller et al. (2007) found that ADHD youths with comorbid generalized anxiety disorder, separation anxiety disorder, and/or social phobia exhibited significantly greater reductions in both ADHD and anxiety symptoms after a 12-week trial of atomoxetine relative to placebo.

Similarly, initial evidence suggests promising outcomes for children with ADHD and ODD or CD treated with medication or multimodal treatments. In the MTA, children with ADHD and ODD/CD responded best to medication (with or without behavioral treatments), while those with ADHD, anxiety, *and* ODD/CD demonstrated the best outcomes when treated with the combined intervention (Jensen et al., 2001). Several studies have demonstrated that atomoxetine results in a significant diminution of ADHD symptoms, yet it is unclear whether this agent impacts ODD symptoms among young people with both disorders (Bangs et al., 2008). Children with ADHD and comorbid aggression may benefit from methylphenidate employed alone or in combination with fluoxetine (Patel & Barzman, 2013). Aggressive symptoms can also be targeted separately with medications such as risperidone, lithium, valproic acid, clonidine, and guanfacine (Patel & Barzman, 2013), though few studies have evaluated the efficacy of these agents specifically for children with ADHD and aggression.

Many families of young people with ADHD and comorbid tics may have questions or concerns about psychotropic medications, particularly the stimulants, which traditionally had been believed to cause or exacerbate tics. Historically, physicians were warned against prescribing methylphenidate to children with co-occurring ADHD and tic disorders because of several uncontrolled case reports and retrospective chart reviews that emerged between the 1960s and 1980s linking stimulant medication and subsequent tic onset or exacerbation (Tourette's Syndrome Study Group, 2002). However, recent prospective controlled trials have challenged these earlier assumptions and have shaped the contemporary understanding that stimulants are not likely to evoke or exacerbate tics. In a randomized double-blind clinical trial conducted by the Tourette's Syndrome Study Group (2002), children with co-occurring ADHD and chronic tic disorder demonstrated significant improvements when treated with methylphenidate or clonidine, with a combination of the two drugs yielding the greatest clinical benefits. Moreover, those receiving methylphenidate, clonidine, or a combination did not evidence exacerbation of tics relative to the placebo group.

Recent research has suggested that several pharmacological approaches may likewise be beneficial for young people with ADHD and comorbid depression. Two clinical trials have revealed that atomoxetine is effective for managing ADHD symptoms but has limited impact on depressive symptoms among children with comorbid ADHD and depression (Bangs et al., 2007; Kratochvil et al., 2005). In one of these studies (Kratochvil et al., 2005), young people with ADHD and comorbid depression or anxiety were treated with fluoxetine or placebo for 8 weeks followed by the addition of adjunctive atomoxetine for the last 5 weeks. Both groups demonstrated similar responses with regard to ADHD symptoms, yet a significantly greater proportion of children who received fluoxetine combined with atomoxetine showed improvements in depression. These results indicate that the combination of atomoxetine and fluoxetine may be effective for treating youth with co-occurring ADHD and depression. Additionally, initial evidence from small open-label studies suggests that bupropion as well as the combination of fluoxetine and methylphenidate may be effective for treating both depressive and ADHD symptoms (Bond et al., 2012). However, given that improvements in one disorder may elicit improvements in the other, experts in the Texas Children's Medication Algorithm Project (CMAP) recommend the initial use of a single medication to target the more severe symptoms of a disorder prior to implementing medication combinations (Pliszka et al., 2006). Emslie and colleagues (2004) note that the CMAP pharmacotherapy algorithm works relatively well for young people with ADHD and depression in a community setting yet also highlight the need for careful monitoring.

Single medication should be used to target the more severe disorder before implementing medication combinations

With regard to young people with ADHD and bipolar disorder, there is emerging evidence to suggest that adding stimulants to mood stabilizers effectively manages ADHD symptoms (Bond et al., 2012). For instance, adjunctive atomoxetine or methylphenidate therapy may yield improvement in ADHD symptoms without destabilizing mood or producing other untoward side effects (Chang, Nayar, Howe, & Rana, 2009; Findling et al., 2007; Scheffer, Kowatch, Carmody, & Rush, 2005). While some retrospective analyses have suggested potential adverse consequences of stimulants in individuals with bipolar disorder, larger prospective studies reveal that the risk of worsened mood following stimulant treatment is low (Miller, Chang, & Ketter, 2013). Evidence-based guidelines for youth with co-occurring ADHD and bipolar disorder suggest using mood-stabilizing agents prior to adding stimulants or atomoxetine in order to attenuate ADHD symptoms without significantly increasing risk for mood destabilization (Miller et al., 2013).

As noted previously, research does not substantiate an association between therapeutic use of stimulant medication and risk for SUDs. Nevertheless, given the addictive potential of stimulants, practitioners should be judicious when prescribing stimulants for children with substance-abusing family members or for adolescents with comorbid CD or substance abuse (Kollins, 2008). For adolescents with co-occurring ADHD and SUDs, Wilens (2006) suggests initially prioritizing treatment of the SUD prior to targeting ADHD symptoms. In circumstances where drug abuse or diversion are relevant risk factors, long-acting stimulants may be useful given that they are less prone to diversion and

Practitioners should be careful when prescribing stimulants for children with substance-abusing family members or for adolescents with comorbid CD or substance abuse

reduce the likelihood of abuse and overdose (Antshel et al., 2011). Given the potential for drug interactions with abused substances, α-agonists and tricyclic antidepressants are generally reserved as alternatives for adolescents with ADHD and comorbid SUDs, given that these agents do not have potential for abuse (Wilens, 2006).

For children with ADHD and LDs, a comprehensive, multimodal treatment approach comprising medication and psychoeducational interventions is the treatment of choice (DuPaul, Gormley, & Laracy, 2013). While psychotropic medications (primarily stimulants) are commonly used with comorbid ADHD and LD and may increase academic productivity, DuPaul and colleagues (2013) caution that psychopharmacology is generally insufficient for addressing the breadth of challenges associated with both ADHD and LD. One recent trial found that methylphenidate yielded significant improvements in ADHD symptoms, cognitive skills, academic task performance, and observed classroom behavior in children both with and without comorbid LD (Williamson, Murray, Damaraju, Ascher, & Starr, 2014). Nonetheless, learning and academic skill deficits likely require intensive, direct instructions that go beyond the behavior modification strategies typically used to treat ADHD (DuPaul et al., 2013). Additionally, children with comorbid ADHD and LD demonstrate optimal outcomes when interventions addressing behavioral and skills deficits are delivered across settings (i.e., home and school). Cross-setting collaboration may be facilitated by conjoint behavior consultation among parents, teachers, and a mental health or educational specialist (DuPaul et al., 2013). Interventions that have demonstrated efficacy in improving academic functioning among students with ADHD include organizational skills training, CAI, peer tutoring, and consultation-based academic interventions. Nonetheless, further research is needed to examine the efficacy of these intervention strategies for young people with ADHD and co-occurring LD (DuPaul et al., 2013).

4.7   Problems in Carrying Out the Treatments

Comorbid psychiatric disorders complicate treatment of young people with ADHD

Clinicians may face many challenges when treating children and adolescents with ADHD. As noted in Chapter 1, a large proportion of young people with ADHD have comorbid psychiatric disorders. Given this complexity, clinicians must navigate the selection of appropriate treatments, including the sequencing, intensity, and duration of interventions. In considering pharmacological interventions, clinicians must carefully weigh the benefits and risks of the various medications used in the management of ADHD. Although many individuals benefit from stimulant medication, adverse side effects (e.g., insomnia, loss of appetite or weight, headaches) are frequently reported. Additionally, there is evidence to suggest that stimulants may interfere with healthy growth (e.g., height, weight). As such, children's growth and development should be closely monitored while being treated with stimulants. Minimizing the risk and maximizing the benefit of treatment requires careful monitoring and adjustment in the dosage and timing of medications. For instance, changing the dose or type of medication may ameliorate some adverse effects, while administering stimulants after breakfast and dinner may help minimize appetite disturbances.

Perhaps the greatest barrier to effective management of ADHD in pediatric populations is poor adherence. About half of children in community settings discontinue prescribed stimulants within the first 3 months (Marcus, Wan, Kemner, & Olfson, 2005). During adolescence, medication adherence rates drop substantially throughout the United States from 72% at age 11 to 32% at 15 years (Barbaresi et al., 2006). Treatment adherence is worse in adolescence due to peer group conformity and adolescents' need for autonomy. Adolescents are often embarrassed at having to receive medication, particularly during the school day, which is why the longer-acting agents are usually prescribed. Because poor treatment adherence contributes to suboptimal medication response, physicians should assist children and their families in the identification of problem-solving barriers in adhering to treatment recommendations. Research suggests that addressing caregiver beliefs may be essential to facilitate optimal adherence, as caregivers are typically responsible for the treatment regimen of their children. Children whose caregivers believe that ADHD symptoms are temperamental or stress-related are less likely to be adherent, while those who understand that ADHD is a neurodevelopmental disorder and believe that medications are safe and effective are likely to be more adherent to their child's treatment regimen (dosReis et al., 2009). In addition to caregiver parental beliefs and attitudes, adherence may be compromised when family members disagree on treatment plans or when there are parent–child relationship problems. Clinicians should evaluate and address problematic family dynamics and motivational factors at the outset of treatment to increase the likelihood of compliance.

> Lack of adherence to the treatment plan by the child and his/her family is common, and can compromise successful treatment

4.8   Efficacy and Prognosis

Numerous controlled clinical trials support the beneficial effects of stimulant medication in improving the core symptoms of ADHD, at least in the short-term. In fact, the use of stimulant medication is one of the most well-documented therapies in all of child psychiatry. For example, double-blind placebo-controlled clinical trials have demonstrated stimulants to be more effective than placebo for enhancing attention and concentration, and for diminishing hyperactivity and impulsivity for children with ADHD (for a review, see Brown & Daly, 2009). Responders to stimulant medication also demonstrate increased on-task behavior and improved academic productivity. Moreover, children treated with stimulants are more consistent in following instructions and rules as well as in reducing verbal and physically aggressive behavior. In general, these studies have demonstrated large effect sizes for reducing impairments associated with the core symptoms of ADHD. Stimulant medication has been found to be effective in 75% of cases. For these reasons, stimulants are considered the first-line option of medication when treating children with ADHD (Wolraich et al., 2011).

As mentioned previously, there are some notable limitations to stimulant treatment. First, approximately 20–30% of children initially will not respond

> Stimulant medication improves the core symptoms of ADHD in the short-term

to stimulant medication. Second, although stimulant medications are generally well-tolerated, some children will experience adverse effects and will need to discontinue the medication. Third, stimulants have a time-limited effect, with the longest acting formulation of stimulant medication designed to last for only 12 hr. Fourth, the behavior of children with ADHD receiving stimulant treatment is rarely normalized, and some children will display significant behavior or attention problems when the effects of the medication dissipate. Fifth, despite the efficacy of stimulant medication, many children and their caregivers prefer nonmedical treatment options. However, caregivers will provide a higher acceptability rating when medication is used in combination with psychosocial/behavioral treatments. Sixth, there is less evidence of efficacy of stimulant medications when used for preschool populations suspected with ADHD. Seventh, with the exception of the MTA, there also is limited evidence regarding long-term effects of stimulant medications, as most clinical trials have been conducted only over very short periods of time and with little follow-up (Wilens et al., 2000). Finally, even though ADHD is a chronic disorder with symptoms that persist for many into adulthood, long-term use of stimulant medications is rare.

> There is limited evidence regarding the long-term effects of stimulant medication

Despite a plethora of research that demonstrates the efficacy of stimulant medications for impairments associated with ADHD, no specific stimulant medication for ADHD has been demonstrated to be more effective than another for alleviating some of the symptoms associated with ADHD. There also seem to be few differences across stimulant medications with regard to adverse side effects. Different formulations work best for different children. Often, children who do not experience a decrease in ADHD symptoms after receiving one stimulant medication may respond well to another. No behavioral or diagnostic predictor has been demonstrated to predict response to stimulant medication. In the event that a child with ADHD does not respond to a stimulant, a second option with regard to medication is the nonstimulants including antidepressants or the α-adrenergics or atomoxetine. The nonstimulants have not been studied for as long or as intensively as the stimulants. In addition, findings from studies generally reveal smaller effect sizes for nonstimulant medication than for the stimulants. According to the AAP (Wolraich et al., 2011), the evidence for nonstimulants is strongest for atomoxetine, decreases for extended-release guanfacine, and is lowest for extended-release clonidine.

> Often children who do not respond to one stimulant medication may respond well to another

In contrast to the recommendation of stimulant medication as a first-line treatment option for school-aged children with ADHD, behavior therapy (e.g., parent behavior training) is considered a first-line treatment option for preschool-aged children (Charach et al., 2013; Klein, Ho, Tazkarji, & Auten, 2013; Wolraich et al., 2011). Medication options are considered when there is insufficient symptomatic improvement after an adequate trial of behavior therapy and when the child experiences moderate to significant levels of impairment (Wolraich et al., 2011). For adolescents with ADHD, the AAP (Wolraich et al., 2011) guidelines suggest treatment with FDA-approved medication for the disorder and the potential adjunct of behavioral therapy.

> Behavior therapies are considered the first-line treatment option for pre-school age children with ADHD

Well-established and evidence-based nonpharmacological treatments for ADHD in children and adolescents include BPT, behavioral classroom management, behavioral peer interventions, and organizational skills training

(Evans et al., 2014). To meet criteria for evidence-based treatment, studies must have been conducted with the following criteria: (1) careful specification of the target population; (2) random assignment to treatment conditions; (3) use of treatment manuals; (4) multiple outcomes with blind raters; (5) appropriate statistical analyses performed; (6) statistically significant differences between the treatment and comparison group at posttreatment demonstrated in at least two research settings; and finally (7) replication by independent researchers (Chambless et al., 1996; Evans et al., 2014; Silverman & Hinshaw, 2008).

There have been several recent meta-analyses of behavior modification for children with ADHD. In a meta-analysis conducted by Fabiano and colleagues (2009), effect sizes were found to be moderate to large depending on the type of study design. For example, the effect sizes for between-group studies was 0.83, for pre-post studies was 0.70, for within-group studies was 2.64, and for single-subject designs was 3.78. Based on these findings, it is concluded that the evidence for behavioral treatments is strong and consistent. Another meta-analysis, conducted by Lee and colleagues (2012) examining the effect of BPT on outcomes associated with child ADHD, reported moderate effect sizes for the majority of outcome variables at posttreatment, but a relatively small effect size at follow-up. A meta-analysis investigating the effects of school-based interventions (e.g., contingency management, academic intervention, cognitive behavior intervention) for young people with ADHD found mean effect sizes for behavioral outcomes according to the following study designs: within-subjects (0.72) and single-subject (2.20). Nonsignificant findings were reported for between-subject designs (0.18; DuPaul, Eckert, & Vilardo, 2012). In terms of academic outcomes, mean effect sizes were positive and significant only for single-subject designs (3.48). Positive but nonsignificant effect sizes were found for between-subject (0.43) and within-subject designs (0.42). A recent meta-analysis of the effect of behavioral parental interventions for preschool children with ADHD yielded a mean effect size of 0.61 compared with control conditions (Mulqueen, Bartley, & Bloch, 2013).

Combined treatment demonstrates many advantages relative to medication alone or psychosocial/behavioral treatment alone. Findings from the MTA reveal rates of normalization of behavior that were 34% for behavior therapy, 56% for medication, and 68% for combined treatments (Swanson et al., 2001). Combined treatment is also recommended as the treatment of choice for children with internalizing disorders and for those from low-income families. Families report higher levels of acceptability for combined treatment than for medication alone. In addition, combined treatment may enhance adherence to treatment. Finally, combining treatments may lessen the medication dose needed to achieve optimal outcomes. Fabiano and colleagues (2007) reported that low dose behavior therapy combined with low dose medication achieved the same effect as high dose medication or high dose behavior therapy alone.

Findings from several meta-analyses indicate that the effect sizes for combined pharmacological and behavioral treatment are large for ADHD symptoms in children (Majewicz-Hefley & Carlson, 2007; Van der Oord, Prins, Oosterlaan, & Emmelkamp, 2008). Results from the meta-analysis completed by Majewicz-Hefley and Carlson (2007) also reveal large effect sizes for the

Behavioral parent training, behavioral classroom management, behavioral peer interventions, and organizational skills training are effective for school-aged children with ADHD

Combined treatment demonstrates many advantages relative to medication alone or psychosocial/ behavioral treatment alone

impact of combined treatment on social skills, but relatively small effect sizes for academic performance. Van der Oord and colleagues (2008) reported no significant impact of combined treatments (i.e., methylphenidate and psychosocial treatments) for academic performance, but moderate effect sizes for social behavior and parent ratings of ODD/CD symptoms.

Few studies have investigated the long-term prognosis of individuals with ADHD as a function of treatment modality. A recent systematic review of randomized controlled trials greater than 1 year in length for the management of ADHD in children and adolescents only identified eight trials that met criteria (Parker, Wales, Chalhoub, & Harpin, 2013). Findings revealed moderate- to high-level evidence that combined interventions and pharmacological interventions employed alone can reduce the core symptoms of ADHD and improve academic performance at 14 months. Parker et al. (2013) suggested that effect sizes may diminish after this period of time. Langberg and Becker (2012) conducted a review of the long-term (3 years or longer) impact of treatment on academic outcomes. Findings from studies revealed that treatment for ADHD improved academic achievement scores, but the effects were smaller for school grades. Finally, a review that examined the long-term (2 years or longer) impact of any treatment (pharmacological, nonpharmacological, or multimodal) versus no treatment for young people with ADHD found that treatment reduced many negative outcomes associated with ADHD; however, those with ADHD were not "normalized" (Shaw et al., 2012).

Owens et al. (2003) have employed data from the MTA to examine variables that might help in predicting response to ADHD treatment for children. Although the investigators did not find any reliable predictors, their findings did suggest some variables that moderate responses to treatment. These variables included parental symptoms of depression, severity of ADHD symptoms, and children's intellectual functioning.

4.9   Multicultural Issues

Females, minorities, and children from low-income backgrounds are underrepresented in studies of ADHD

Research on ADHD treatments has largely focused on interventions delivered to White males from middle- to upper-middle-class families. Females, minorities, and children from low socioeconomic backgrounds are significantly underrepresented in clinical trials of ADHD treatments, and thus relatively less is known regarding effective management for these young people. The few studies that have examined gender differences generally indicate comparable responsiveness to behavioral treatment and stimulant medication. Single-parent status, low socioeconomic status, and lower parental education are associated with poorer compliance with medication and parent training and thereby less favorable outcomes. In addition, there is evidence to suggest that minority children are less likely to receive stimulant treatment relative to their White counterparts, though recent investigations have suggested that those who do receive stimulants exhibit comparable treatment responses to their White peers. While culture may impact the way in which ADHD is understood and managed, a recent study suggests that willingness to use ADHD interventions was not associated with children's race, sex, or socioeconomic status (Bussing et al., 2012). Clearly, additional research is necessary to better understand how diversity and culture influence ADHD management and to promote the development of culturally competent services for this population.

5

Case Vignettes

5.1 Lakisha (preschool)

Lakisha is a 4-year-old African American girl who arrived at her pediatrician's office with her mother, Jennifer. Jennifer was concerned that Lakisha was overly active and had difficulty following directions. Although Jennifer had been frustrated with Lakisha's behavior, it was family relatives and Lakisha's preschool teacher who suggested that the mother bring Lakisha to the pediatrician for an evaluation.

Lakisha's father, Damon, is separated from Jennifer. Her parents separated when Lakisha was 2 years of age. Damon lives in a neighborhood about 30 minutes away. He has only sporadic contact with Lakisha, meeting with her approximately four times a year. Lakisha lives with her two older brothers (ages 7 and 11 years), one younger sister (age 6 months), and her maternal grandmother. Because Jennifer works a full-time job, many of the caregiving duties are completed by Lakisha's grandmother.

Jennifer reported that she was generally healthy during her pregnancy with Lakisha. She was delivered 1 month prematurely via cesarean section due to a breech position at birth. Lakisha was jaundiced at birth and was also incubated (without a respirator). Lakisha was a colicky infant who was difficult to feed, but has had no other major problems after birth and has been healthy except for a few ear infections as a toddler. Lakisha met all developmental milestones on time.

In the physical exam by her pediatrician, Dr. Thomas, Lakisha was found to be in the 55th percentile for height, weight, and head circumference. Vital signs, vision screening, and hearing screening were normal, and she had no dysmorphic features. The only dermatological finding was pierced ears. Her neurological exam was normal. Lakisha was friendly and answered questions willingly for Dr. Thomas. He did observe that Lakisha had trouble sitting still, although was able to be redirected.

Jennifer described Lakisha as a very talkative child with endless energy. Lakisha likes to climb on things and run around the house. She is often observed to act impulsively by grabbing toys from her older brothers without asking and by grabbing for sharp objects such as a kitchen knife even though she has repeatedly been told that knives are dangerous. Jennifer also reported that Lakisha struggles to follow directions, especially when they are multistep instructions. For example, if Lakisha is asked to put away her toys and to get dressed, she frequently only completes one of the tasks. Both Jennifer and Lakisha's grandmother are often frustrated with Lakisha's behavior and sometimes resort to yelling at her.

Lakisha's preschool teacher, Mrs. Rose, has told Jennifer that Lakisha has difficulty sustaining attention in school tasks or play activities. Mrs. Rose notes that Lakisha can be distracted easily and that she needs constant redirection throughout the preschool day. Mrs. Rose also reports that Lakisha cannot sit still during circle time and that she frequently tries to run out of the preschool room.

At the end of the office visit, Dr. Thomas provided Jennifer with Conners' Early Childhood (Conners EC) rating scales (Conners, 2009). At Lakisha's next visit, Jennifer brought the completed Conners' ratings scales. After reviewing these, it was determined that Lakisha was in the at-risk range for hyperactivity/impulsivity and inattention on both the parent and teacher versions of the scale. Although Lakisha demonstrated some symptoms of ADHD, and there was evidence of impairment across settings, Dr. Thomas was reluctant to diagnose her with ADHD because some of her behaviors were also developmentally appropriate for a 4-year-old.

Because parent management training is considered the first-line treatment for preschool children with ADHD symptoms, it was decided, in consultation with the mother, that she and Lakisha would be referred to outpatient treatment with a child psychologist who specializes in teaching parent behavior management strategies.

Jennifer's history is typical of many cases of suspected ADHD in preschool children. She had some signs of ADHD, and there was evidence of impairment at home and school. On the other hand, impulsivity and overactivity are also developmentally normative in preschool children, making the diagnosis of ADHD challenging in this age group. Jennifer and Lakisha's grandmother did report difficulty with knowing and implementing the correct strategies to help manage Lakisha's behavior. Therefore, the recommendation to meet with a child psychologist skilled in coaching caregivers on effective behavior management strategies seems to be an appropriate treatment decision.

5.2   Sean (school age)

Sean is a 9-year-old White male who was referred by his pediatrician to a child psychologist for an ADHD evaluation due to caregiver concerns of inattention, distractibility, hyperactivity, lack of focus, and impulsivity.

According to the developmental history and general information provided by the family, Sean met all developmental milestones on time and had had no major injuries or hospitalizations. At home, his caregivers noted that Sean was disorganized, impulsive, easily frustrated, short in attention span, overactive, and distractible. He frequently misplaced items. Socially, he relates well with his peers. He is described as a very competitive child who is easily frustrated and does not like to lose in games. These behaviors reportedly began around age 2 and have generally remained consistent or worsened. Teachers at school have also noted that Sean is inattentive, hyperactive, lacks focus, and has trouble following directions; however, he is not disruptive in the classroom.

Results from the Conners' rating scale (parent version) indicated clinically significant problems with inattention, hyperactivity/impulsivity, executive functioning, and aggression as reported by Sean's caregivers. Results from the

Conners' rating scale (teacher version) indicated clinically significant problems with inattention, hyperactivity/impulsivity, and aggression. Results from the Conners' Continuous Performance Test (CPT II), an objective computer vigilance test that examines sustained attention, revealed that Sean's scores matched a clinical confidence index of 50%, suggesting that there was an equal chance that his profile belonged to a clinical or nonclinical individual. When further examining his scores, there was an indication of challenges with vigilance and sustained attention.

The child psychologist reviewed the results of the psychoeducational testing completed by an independent testing company that revealed that Sean is a very intelligent young man (IQ = 123), and that his academic achievement scores were generally commensurate with his IQ scores, suggesting no evidence of an LD.

In summary, Sean was reportedly hyperactive, inattentive, and impulsive at home and at school. These behaviors were significantly impairing across settings. Based on information from the clinical evaluation and the results of the various rating scales, and an objective measure of inattention and impulsivity, Sean met the DSM-5 criteria for ADHD combined presentation (314.01).

For treatment, the child psychologist recommended that Sean and his family meet with their pediatrician or a child psychiatrist to consider a trial of stimulant medication. Sean was also referred to a social worker to help teach him coping skills in response to losing games with peers.

5.3   Andre (adolescent)

Andre is a 14-year-old biracial freshman student in high school who was referred to a neuropsychologist due to recent academic difficulties. Although he reportedly works hard in school, Andre has received failing grades on his finals in a science and social studies course. During elementary and junior high school, Andre found that he could easily excel in his classes without having to allocate very much time for studying and assignments. He reports having been distracted often during classes and daydreaming during lectures, and often needed to check in with his classmates regarding course material or instructions that he missed. However, Andre explained that he was able to perform well when the course content involved lab work with specific instructions and procedures. He thrives on "hands-on" activities, but often finds reading and essay writing to be difficult. When he was assigned novels in his English classes, he always hoped that there would be a movie he could rent to help him visualize the book's content. After Andre saw the movie, he found it much easier to read and remember passages in the novel. Besides these academic concerns, Andre does not believe that other areas of his life have been especially challenging, except for his difficulties with organization. He has trouble keeping track of important papers, and often loses clothing or other items.

Andre participated in a full assessment for ADHD and learning concerns, which included the Brown ADHD scales (Brown, 2001) and interview, the Behavior Rating Inventory of Executive Function (BRIEF; Gioia, Isquith,

Guy, & Kenworthy, 2013), the Wechsler Intelligence Scale for Children – Fourth Edition (WISC-IV; Wechsler, 2004), the Woodcock Johnson Tests of Achievement – Third Edition (WJ-III; Woodcock, McGrew, & Mather, 2001), the Delis-Kaplan Executive Function System (D-KEFS; Delis et al., 2001), and the TOVA (Greenberg & Waldman, 1993). Andre's mother was able to provide information during the clinical interview about his past and current behaviors. Andre's mother and several of his high school teachers identified his difficulties with organization and a tendency to be easily distracted. Andre also noted these difficulties himself during the interview from the Brown scales. In addition, findings from the BRIEF also revealed significant problems with initiation, shifting, working memory, organization of materials, and monitoring. His TOVA, D-KEFS, and WISC-IV scores were consistent with those of individuals with ADHD. Results from the WJ-III achievement measure were not below grade level and therefore did not suggest the presence of a specific LD. Following this assessment, Andre was diagnosed with ADHD inattentive presentation and was referred to a psychiatrist, who prescribed Adderall to target his attentional difficulties. Andre was also referred to a child psychologist who specialized in executive function strategies.

Andre's case is typical of many new high school students who manage to perform adequately during elementary and junior school but struggle to adjust to more demanding academic and social expectations during high school. If behavioral issues are not present throughout their school-age years, this type of student may go "under the radar" and not be referred for an evaluation for a diagnosis of ADHD. When appropriately identified, these types of students may be helped by psychosocial and pharmacological interventions.

6

Further Reading

Barkley, R. A. (2014). *Attention-deficit hyperactivity disorder: A handbook for diagnosis and treatment* (4th ed.). New York, NY: Guilford Press.
This book is widely regarded as the standard clinical reference for ADHD. It provides current knowledge about ADHD in children, adolescents, and adults, including conceptualizations and evidence-based guidelines for assessment, diagnosis, and treatment approaches in a range of settings. The book examines the impact of the disorder across functional domains such as behavior, learning, school and vocational outcomes, and health. Given the breadth of relevant topics covered, this resource is instrumental for both researchers and clinicians.

Barkley, R. A. (2013). *Taking charge of ADHD: The complete, authoritative guide for parents* (3rd ed.). New York, NY: Guilford Press.
This book synthesizes empirical literature regarding ADHD and effective treatment approaches. It provides resources, tools, and practical, concrete suggestions, including an eight-step behavior management plan specifically designed for children and teens with ADHD. This book aims to help parents make sense of their child's symptoms, obtain an accurate diagnosis, collaborate with school and health care professionals, learn parenting techniques that promote better behavior, and strengthen children's academic and social skills. Though intended for parents, this book may be helpful for clinicians and patients.

Brown, T. E. (2013). *A new understanding of ADHD in children and adults: Executive function impairments*. New York, NY: Routledge.
This book combines recent clinical and neuroscience research into a new explanatory paradigm that emphasizes the role of executive functions in ADHD. Moving beyond behavioral characteristics associated with the disorder, it provides an integrated and comprehensive understanding of the complex brain development and cognitive functioning issues underlying ADHD at various points throughout the lifespan. An engaging and accessible read based in empirical research, this book is a highly useful resource for professionals and clinicians, students, and families.

Dawson, P., & Guare, R. (2009). *Smart but scattered: The revolutionary "executive skills" approach to helping kids reach their potential.* New York, NY: Guilford Press.
This book is written for parents of children with executive function challenges such as trouble completing homework, cleaning up their bedroom, or following instructions at school. Although this book does not focus exclusively on children with ADHD, the strategies, activities, and worksheets included in the book can be helpful in parenting kids with ADHD. The book covers ages 4 to 14 years and provides descriptions of executive function skills such as time management, working memory, and emotional control.

Hallowell, E. M., & Ratey, J. J. (2011). *Driven to distraction: Recognizing and coping with attention deficit disorder.* New York, NY: Random House.
This book provides many case histories and stories of children, adolescents, and adults with ADHD. The authors describe the positives and negatives associated with ADHD. In addition, the authors provide detailed information on all treatment options.

7

References

Abikoff, H., McGough, J., Vitiello, B., McCracken, J., Davies, M., Walkup, J., . . . Ritz, L. (2005). Sequential pharmacotherapy for children with comorbid attention-deficit/hyperactivity and anxiety disorders. *Journal of the American Academy of Child and Adolescent Psychiatry, 44,* 418–427. http://doi.org/10.1097/01.chi.0000155320.52322.37

Abikoff, H. B., Jensen, P. S., Arnold, L. L., Hoza, B., Hechtman, L., Pollack, S., . . . Wigal, T. (2002). Observed classroom behavior of children with ADHD: relationship to gender and comorbidity. *Journal of Abnormal Child Psychology, 30,* 349–359. http://doi.org/10.1023/A:1015713807297

Achenbach, T. M., & Rescorla, L. A. (2001). *Manual for the ASEBA school-age forms & profiles.* Burlington, VT: University of Vermont, Research Center for Children, Youth, & Families.

Adams, G. L. (1984). *Normative Adaptive Behavior Checklist (NABC).* San Antonio, TX: Psychological Corporation.

Ambrosini, P. J. (2000). Historical development and present status of the Schedule for Affective Disorders and Schizophrenia for School-Age Children (K-SADS). *Journal of American Academy of Child and Adolescent Psychiatry, 39*(1), 49–58. http://doi.org/10.1097/00004583-200001000-00016

American Psychiatric Association. (2000). *Diagnostic and statistical manual of mental disorders* (4th ed.). Washington, DC: Author.

American Psychiatric Association. (2013). *Diagnostic and statistical manual of mental disorders* (5th ed.). Arlington, VA: American Psychiatric Publishing.

American Psychiatric Association, Working Group on Psychoactive Medications for Children and Adolescents. (2006). *Psychopharmacological, psychosocial, and combined interventions for childhood disorders: evidence base, contextual factors, and future directions.* Washington, DC: American Psychological Association.

Angold, A., & Costello, E. J. (2000). The Child and Adolescent Psychiatric Assessment (CAPA). *Journal of the American Academy of Child and Adolescent Psychiatry, 39*(1), 39–48. http://doi.org/10.1097/00004583-200001000-00015

Angold, A., Erkanli, A., Egger, H. L., & Costello, E. J. (2000). *Stimulant treatment for children: a community perspective. Journal of the American Academy of Child and Adolescent Psychiatry, 39,* 975–984, discussion 984–994.

Antshel, K. M., Hargrave, T. M., Simonescu, M., Kaul, P., Hendricks, K., & Faraone, S. V. (2011). Advances in understanding and treating ADHD. *BMC Medicine, 9,* 72–83.

Bangs, M. E., Emslie, G. J., Spencer, T. J., Ramsey, J. L., Carlson, C., Bartky, E. J., . . . Sumner, C. R. (2007). Efficacy and safety of atomoxetine in adolescents with attention-deficit/hyperactivity disorder and major depression. *Journal of Child and Adolescent Psychopharmacology, 17,* 407–420. http://doi.org/10.1089/cap.2007.0066

Bangs, M. E., Hazell, P., Danckaerts, M., Hoare, P., Coghill, D. R., Wehmeier, P. M., . . . Levine, L. (2008). Atomoxetine for the treatment of Attention-Deficit/Hyperactivity Disorder and Oppositional Defiant Disorder. *Pediatrics, 121,* e314–e320. http://doi.org/10.1542/peds.2006-1880

Barbaresi, W. J., Katusic, S. K., Colligan, R. C., Pankratz, V. S., Weaver, A. L., Weber, K. J., . . . Jacobsen, S. J. (2002). How common is attention-deficit/hyperactivity disorder? Incidence in a population-based birth cohort in Rochester, Minn. *Archives of Pediatrics & Adolescent Medicine, 156,* 217–224. http://doi.org/10.1001/archpedi.156.3.217

Barbaresi, W. J., Katusic, S. K., Colligan, R. C., Weaver, A. L., & Jacobsen, S. J. (2007). Modifiers of long-term school outcomes for children with attention-deficit/hyperactivity disorder: does treatment with stimulant medication make a difference? Results from a population-based study. *Journal of Developmental and Behavioral Pediatrics, 28,* 274–287. http://doi.org/10.1097/DBP.0b013e3180cabc28

Barbaresi, W. J., Katusic, S. K., Colligan, R. C., Weaver, A. L., Leibson, C. L., & Jacobsen, S. J. (2006). Long-term stimulant medication treatment of attention-deficit/hyperactivity disorder: results from a population-based study. *Journal of Developmental and Behavioral Pediatrics, 27*(1), 1–10. http://doi.org/10.1097/00004703-200602000-00001

Barkley, R. A. (1990). *Attention-deficit hyperactivity disorder: A handbook for diagnosis and treatment.* New York: Guilford Press.

Barkley, R. A. (1997). Behavioral inhibition, sustained attention, and executive functions: Constructing a unifying theory of ADHD. *Psychological Bulletin, 121,* 65–94. http://doi.org/10.1037/0033-2909.121.1.65

Barkley, R. A. (2006). *Attention-deficit hyperactivity: A handbook for diagnosis and treatment* (3rd ed.). New York: Guilford Press.

Barkley, R. A. (2012). *The executive functions: What they are, how they work, and why they evolved.* New York: Guilford Press.

Barkley, R. A., Fischer, M., Smallish, L., & Fletcher, K. (2003). Does the treatment of attention-deficit/hyperactivity disorder with stimulants contribute to drug use/abuse? A 13-year prospective study. *Pediatrics, 111*(1), 97–109. http://doi.org/10.1542/peds.111.1.97

Barkley, R. A., Fischer, M., Smallish, L., & Fletcher, K. (2004). Young adult follow-up of hyperactive children: antisocial activities and drug use. *Journal of Child Psychology and Psychiatry, 45,* 195–211. http://doi.org/10.1111/j.1469-7610.2004.00214.x

Barkley, R. A., Murphy, K. R., & Fischer, M. (2008). *ADHD in adults: What the science says.* New York: Guilford Press.

Barkley, R. A., & Peters, H. (2012). The earliest reference to ADHD in the medical literature? Melchior Adam Weikard's description in 1775 of "attention deficit" (Mangel der Aufmerksamkeit, Attentio Volubilis). *Journal of Attention Disorders, 16,* 623–630. http://doi.org/10.1177/1087054711432309

Bauermeister, J. J., Barkley, R. A., Bauermeister, J. A., Martinez, J. V., & McBurnett, K. (2012). Validity of the sluggish cognitive tempo, inattention, and hyperactivity symptom dimensions: neuropsychological and psychosocial correlates. *Journal of Abnormal Child Psychology, 40,* 683–697. http://doi.org/10.1007/s10802-011-9602-7

Bauermeister, J. J., Canino, G., Polanczyk, G., & Rohde, L. A. (2010). ADHD across cultures: is there evidence for a bidimensional organization of symptoms? *Journal of Clinical Child and Adolescent Psychology, 39,* 362–372. http://doi.org/10.1080/15374411003691743

Beck, S. J., Hanson, C. A., Puffenberger, S. S., Benninger, K. L., & Benninger, W. B. (2010). A controlled trial of working memory training for children and adolescents with ADHD. *Journal of Clinical Child and Adolescent Psychology, 39,* 825–836. http://doi.org/10.1080/15374416.2010.517162

Berg, E. A. (1948). A simple objective technique for measuring flexibility in thinking. *Journal of General Psychology, 39,* 15–22. http://doi.org/10.1080/00221309.1948.9918159

Bhatara, V., Loudenberg, R., & Ellis, R. (2006). Association of attention deficit hyperactivity disorder and gestational alcohol exposure: an exploratory study. *Journal of Attention Disorders, 9,* 515–522. http://doi.org/10.1177/1087054705283880

Biederman, J., & Faraone, S. V. (2002). Current concepts on the neurobiology of Attention-Deficit/Hyperactivity Disorder. *Journal of Attention Disorders, 6*(1), 7–16.

Biederman, J., Monuteaux, M. C., Mick, E., Spencer, T., Wilens, T. E., Silva, J. M., . . . Faraone, S. V. (2006). Young adult outcome of attention deficit hyperactivity disorder: a controlled 10-year follow-up study. *Psychological Medicine, 36*(2), 167–179. http://doi.org/10.1017/S0033291705006410

Biederman, J., Monuteaux, M. C., Spencer, T., Wilens, T. E., & Faraone, S. V. (2009). Do stimulants protect against psychiatric disorders in youth with ADHD? A 10-year follow-up study. *Pediatrics, 124*(1), 71–78. http://doi.org/10.1542/peds.2008-3347

Biederman, J., Swanson, J. M., Wigal, S. B., Kratochvil, C. J., Boellner, S. W., Earl, C. Q., . . . Greenhill, L. (2005). Efficacy and safety of modafinil film-coated tablets in children and adolescents with attention-deficit/hyperactivity disorder: Results of a randomized, double-blind, placebo-controlled, flexible-dose study. *Pediatrics, 116,* e777–e784. http://doi.org/10.1542/peds.2005-0617

Biederman, J., Wilens, T., Mick, E., Spencer, T., & Faraone, S. V. (1999). Pharmacotherapy of attention-deficit/hyperactivity disorder reduces risk for substance use disorder. *Pediatrics, 104*(2), e20–e24. http://doi.org/10.1542/peds.104.2.e20

Bloch, M. H., Panza, K. E., Landeros-Weisenberger, A., & Leckman, J. F. (2009). Meta-analysis: treatment of attention-deficit/hyperactivity disorder in children with comorbid tic disorders. *Journal of the American Academy of Child and Adolescent Psychiatry, 48,* 884–893. http://doi.org/10.1097/CHI.0b013e3181b26e9f

Bond, D. J., Hadjipavlou, G., Lam, R. W., McIntyre, R. S., Beaulieu, S., Schaffer, A., & Weiss, M. (2012). The Canadian Network for Mood and Anxiety Treatments (CANMAT) task force recommendations for the management of patients with mood disorders and comorbid attention-deficit/hyperactivity disorder. *Annals of Clinical Psychiatry, 24*(1), 23–37.

Brock, S. E., Jimerson, S. R., & Hansen, R. (2009). Identifying, assessing, and treating attention deficit hyperactivity disorder (ADHD) at school. In S. Jimerson & S. Brock (Eds.), *Developmental psychopathology at school.* New York: Springer Science.

Brown, R. T., Amler, R. W., Freeman, W. S., Perrin, J. M., Stein, M. T., Feldman, H. M., . . . Wolraich, M. L. (2005). Treatment of Attention-Deficit/Hyperactivity Disorder: Overview of the evidence. *Pediatrics, 115,* e749–e757. http://doi.org/10.1542/peds.2004-2560

Brown, R. T., & Daly, B. P. (2009). Neuropsychological effects of stimulant medication on children's learning and behavior. In C. R. Reynolds & E. Fletcher-Janzen (Eds.), *Handbook of clinical child neuropsychology* (3rd ed., pp. 529–580). New York: Plenum.

Brown, T. E. (2001). *Brown Attention-Deficit Disorder Scales.* San Antonio, TX: Pearson Assessments.

Burt, S. A., Krueger, R. F., McGue, M., & Iacono, W. (2003). Parent-child conflict and the comorbidity among childhood externalizing disorders. *Archives of General Psychiatry, 60,* 505–513. http://doi.org/10.1001/archpsyc.60.5.505

Bussing, R., Koro-Ljungberg, M., Noguchi, K., Mason, D., Mayerson, G., & Garvan, C. W. (2012). Willingness to use ADHD treatments: A mixed methods study of perceptions by adolescents, parents, health professionals and teachers. *Social Science & Medicine, 74*(1), 92–100. http://doi.org/10.1016/j.socscimed.2011.10.009

Calipari, E. S., & Ferris, M. J. (2013). Amphetamine mechanisms and actions at the dopamine terminal revisited. *The Journal of Neuroscience, 33,* 8923–8925. http://doi.org/10.1523/JNEUROSCI.1033-13.2013

Chambless, D. L., Sanderson, W. C., Shoham, V., Bennett Johnson, S., Pope, K. S., Crits-Christoph, P., . . . McCurry, S. (1996). An update on empirically validated therapies. *The Clinical Psychologist, 49,* 5–18.

Chang, K., Nayar, D., Howe, M., & Rana, M. (2009). Atomoxetine as an adjunct therapy in the treatment of co-morbid attention-deficit/hyperactivity disorder in children and adolescents with bipolar I or II disorder. *Journal of Child and Adolescent Psychopharmacology, 19,* 547–551. http://doi.org/10.1089/cap.2009.0030

Charach, A., Carson, P., Fox, S., Ali, M. U., Beckett, J., & Lim, C. G. (2013). Interventions for preschool children at high risk for ADHD: A comparative effectiveness review. *Pediatrics, 131,* E1584–E1604. http://doi.org/10.1542/peds.2012-0974

Chi, T. C., & Hinshaw, S. P. (2002). Mother-child relationships of children with ADHD: The role of maternal depressive symptoms and depression-related distortions. *Journal of Abnormal Child Psychology, 30,* 387–400. http://doi.org/10.1023/A:1015770025043

Chronis, A. M., Chacko, A., Fabiano, G. A., Wymbs, B. T., & Pelham, W. E., Jr. (2004). Enhancements to the behavioral parent training paradigm for families of children with ADHD: Review and future directions. *Clinical Child and Family Psychology Review, 7*(1), 1–27. http://doi.org/10.1023/B:CCFP.0000020190.60808.a4

Clarfield, J., & Stoner, G. (2005). The effects of computerized reading instruction on the academic performance of students identified with ADHD. *School Psychology Review, 34,* 246–254.

Cohen, M. (1997). *Children's Memory Scale.* San Antonio, TX: Psychological Corporation.

Connor, D. F. (2011, August 11). Problems of overdiagnosis and overprescribing in ADHD. *Psychiatric Times.* Retrieved from http://www.psychiatrictimes.com/adhd/problems-overdiagnosis-and-overprescribing-adhd/page/0/1

Conners, C. K. (2000). *Conners' Continuous Performance Test II (CPTII).* New York: Multi-Health Systems.

Conners, C. K. (2008). *Conners' Rating Scales* (3rd ed.). New York: Multi-Health Systems.

Conners, C. K. (2009). *Conners' Early Childhood Rating Scales.* New York: Multi-Health Systems.

Corkum, P., Rimer, P., & Schachar, R. (1999). Parental knowledge of attention-deficit hyperactivity disorder and opinions of treatment options: Impact on enrolment and adherence to a 12-month treatment trial. *Canadian Journal of Psychiatry, 44,* 1043–1048.

Corkum, P., Tannock, R., Moldofsky, H., Hogg-Johnson, S., & Humphries, T. (2001). Actigraphy and parental ratings of sleep in children with attention-deficit/hyperactivity disorder (ADHD). *Sleep, 24,* 303–312.

Cornelius, M. D., & Day, N. L. (2009). Developmental consequences of prenatal tobacco exposure. *Current Opinion in Neurology, 22*(2), 121–125. http://doi.org/10.1097/WCO.0b013e328326f6dc

Cortese, S., Kelly, C., Chabernaud, C., Proal, E., Di Martino, A., Milham, M. P., & Castellanos, F. X. (2012). Toward systems neuroscience of ADHD: A meta-analysis of 55 fMRI studies. *American Journal of Psychiatry, 169,* 1038–1055. http://doi.org/10.1176/appi.ajp.2012.11101521

Counts, C. A., Nigg, J. T., Stawicki, J. A., Rappley, M. D., & Von Eye, A. (2005). Family adversity in DSM-IV ADHD combined and inattentive subtypes and associated disruptive behavior problems. *Journal of the American Academy of Child and Adolescent Psychiatry, 44,* 690–698. http://doi.org/10.1097/01.chi.0000162582.87710.66

Daly, B. P., Creed, T., Xanthopoulos, M., & Brown, R. T. (2007). Psychosocial treatments for children with attention deficit/hyperactivity disorder. *Neuropsychol Review, 17*(1), 73–89. http://doi.org/10.1007/s11065-006-9018-2

Delis, D. C., Kaplan, E., & Kramer, J. (2001). *Delis-Kaplan Executive Function System.* San Antonio, TX: Psychological Corporation.

Delis, D. C., Kramer, J. H., Kaplan, E., & Ober, B. A. (1994). *Manual for the California Verbal Learning Test Manual: Children's version.* San Antonio, TX: Psychological Corporation.

Denckla, M. B. (2000). Learning disabilities and attention-deficit/hyperactivity disorder in adults: Overlap with executive dysfunction. In T. E. Brown (Ed.), *Attention-deficit disorders and comorbidities in children, adolescents, and adults* (pp. 297–318). Washington, DC: American Psychiatric Press.

dosReis, S., Mychailyszyn, M. P., Evans-Lacko, S. E., Beltran, A., Riley, A. W., & Myers, M. A. (2009). The meaning of attention-deficit/hyperactivity disorder medication and parents' initiation and continuity of treatment for their child. *Journal of Child and Adolescent Psychopharmacology, 19,* 377–383. http://doi.org/10.1089/cap.2008.0118

DuPaul, G. J., Eckert, T. L., & Vilardo, B. (2012). The effects of school-based interventions for attention deficit hyperactivity disorder: A meta-analysis. *School Psychology Review, 41,* 387–412.

DuPaul, G. J., Gormley, M. J., & Laracy, S. D. (2013). Comorbidity of LD and ADHD: Implications of DSM-5 for assessment and treatment. *Journal of Learning Disabilities, 46*(1), 43–51.

DuPaul, G. J., Power, T. J., Anastopoulos, A. D., & Reid, R. (1998). *ADHD Rating Scale-IV: Checklists, norms, and clinical interpretation.* New York: Guilford Press.

Eddy, C. M., Cavanna, A. E., Gulisano, M., Agodi, A., Barchitta, M., Cali, P., . . . Rizzo, R. (2011). Clinical correlates of quality of life in Tourette syndrome. *Movement Disorders, 26,* 735–738. http://doi.org/10.1002/mds.23434

Eiraldi, R. B., Mautone, J. A., & Power, T. J. (2012). Strategies for implementing evidence-based psychosocial interventions for children with attention-deficit/hyperactivity disorder. *Child and Adolescent Psychiatric Clinics of North America, 21*(1), 145–159. http://doi.org/10.1016/j.chc.2011.08.012

Emslie, G. J., Hughes, C. W., Crismon, M. L., Lopez, M., Pliszka, S. R., Toprac, M. G., & Boemer, C. (2004). A feasibility study of the childhood depression medication algorithm: the Texas Children's Medication Algorithm Project (CMAP). *Journal of the American Academy of Child and Adolescent Psychiatry, 43,* 519–527. http://doi.org/10.1097/00004583-200405000-00005

Evans, S. W., Owens, J. S., & Bunford, N. (2014). Evidence-based psychosocial treatments for children and adolescents with attention-deficit/hyperactivity disorder. *Journal of Clinical Child and Adolescent Psychology, 43,* 527–551. http://doi.org/10.1080/15374416.2013.850700

Fabiano, G. A. (2011). Assessment of children and adolescents with attention deficit hyperactivity disorder. In S. W. Evans & B. Hoza (Eds.), *Treating attention deficit hyperactivity disorder: Assessment and intervention in a developmental context.* Kingston, NJ: Civic Research Institute.

Fabiano, G. A., Pelham, W. E., Gnagy, E. M., Burrows-MacLean, L., Coles, E. K., Chacko, A., . . . Robb, J. A. (2007). The single and combined effects of multiple intensities of behavior modification and methylphenidate for children with attention deficit hyperactivity disorder in a classroom setting. *School Psychology Review, 36*(2), 195–216.

Fabiano, G. A., Pelham, W. E., Jr., Coles, E. K., Gnagy, E. M., Chronis-Tuscano, A., & O'Connor, B. C. (2009). A meta-analysis of behavioral treatments for attention-deficit/hyperactivity disorder. *Clinical Psychology Review, 29*(2), 129–140.

Fabiano, G. A., Pelham, W. E., Jr., Waschbusch, D. A., Gnagy, E. M., Lahey, B. B., Chronis, A. M., . . . Burrows-Maclean, L. (2006). A practical measure of impairment: psychometric properties of the impairment rating scale in samples of children with attention deficit hyperactivity disorder and two school-based samples. *Journal of Clinical Child and Adolescent Psychology, 35,* 369–385. http://doi.org/10.1207/s15374424jccp3503_3

Fabiano, G. A., Vujnovic, R. K., Pelham, W. E., Waschbusch, D. A., Massetti, G. M., Pariseau, M. E., . . . Volker, M. (2010). Enhancing the effectiveness of special education programming for children with Attention Deficit Hyperactivity Disorder using a daily report card. *School Psychology Review, 39,* 219–239.

Faraone, S. V. (2009). Using meta-analysis to compare the efficacy of medications for attention-deficit/hyperactivity disorder in youths. *P&T, 34,* 678–694.

Faraone, S. V., & Buitelaar, J. (2010). Comparing the efficacy of stimulants for ADHD in children and adolescents using meta-analysis. *European Child & Adolescent Psychiatry, 19,* 353–364. http://doi.org/10.1007/s00787-009-0054-3

Faraone, S. V., & Mick, E. (2010). Molecular genetics of attention deficit hyperactivity disorder. *Psychiatric Clinics of North America, 33*(1), 159–180. http://doi.org/10.1016/j.psc.2009.12.004

Faraone, S. V., Perlis, R. H., Doyle, A. E., Smoller, J. W., Goralnick, J. J., Holmgren, M. A., & Sklar, P. (2005). Molecular genetics of attention-deficit/hyperactivity disorder. *Biological Psychiatry, 57,* 1313–1323. http://doi.org/10.1016/j.biopsych.2004.11.024

Fiks, A. G., Mayne, S., Hughes, C. C., Debartolo, E., Behrens, C., Guevara, J. P., & Power, T. (2012). Development of an instrument to measure parents' preferences and goals for the treatment of attention deficit-hyperactivity disorder. *Academic Pediatrics, 12,* 445–455. http://doi.org/10.1016/j.acap.2012.04.009

Findling, R. L. (1996). Open-label treatment of comorbid depression and attentional disorders with co-administration of serotonin reuptake inhibitors and psychostimulants in children, adolescents, and adults: a case series. *Journal of Child and Adolescent Psychopharmacology, 6*(3), 165–175. http://doi.org/10.1089/cap.1996.6.165

Findling, R. L., Short, E. J., McNamara, N. K., Demeter, C. A., Stansbrey, R. J., Gracious, B. L., . . . Calabrese, J. R. (2007). Methylphenidate in the treatment of children and adolescents with bipolar disorder and attention-deficit/hyperactivity disorder. *Journal of the American Academy of Child and Adolescent Psychiatry, 46,* 1445–1453. http://doi.org/10.1097/chi.0b013e31814b8d3b

Ford, J. D., Racusin, R., Ellis, C. G., Daviss, W. B., Reiser, J., Fleischer, A., & Thomas, J. (2000). Child maltreatment, other trauma exposure, and posttraumatic symptomatology among children with Oppositional Defiant and Attention Deficit Hyperactivity Disorders. *Child Maltreatment, 5,* 205–217. http://doi.org/10.1177/1077559500005003001

Forero, D. A., Arboleda, G. H., Vasquez, R., & Arboleda, H. (2009). Candidate genes involved in neural plasticity and the risk for attention-deficit hyperactivity disorder: a meta-analysis of 8 common variants. *Journal of Psychiatry and Neuroscience, 34,* 361–366.

Frazier, T. W., Demaree, H. A., & Youngstrom, E. A. (2004). Meta-analysis of intellectual and neuropsychological test performance in attention-deficit/hyperactivity disorder. *Neuropsychology, 18,* 543–555. http://doi.org/10.1037/0894-4105.18.3.543

Froehlich, T. E., Lanphear, B. P., Epstein, J. N., Barbaresi, W. J., Katusic, S. K., & Kahn, R. S. (2007). Prevalence, recognition, and treatment of attention-deficit/hyperactivity disorder in a national sample of US children. *Archives of Pediatrics & Adolescent Medicine, 161,* 857–864. http://doi.org/10.1001/archpedi.161.9.857

Gadow, K. D., Drabick, D. A. G., Loney, J., Sprafkin, J., Salisbury, H., Azizian, A., & Schwartz, J. (2004). Comparison of ADHD symptom subtypes as source-specific syndromes. *Journal of Child Psychology and Psychiatry, 45,* 1135–1149. http://doi.org/10.1111/j.1469-7610.2004.00306.x

Galera, C., Cote, S. M., Bouvard, M. P., Pingault, J. B., Melchior, M., Michel, G., . . . Tremblay, R. E. (2011). Early risk factors for hyperactivity-impulsivity and inattention trajectories from age 17 months to 8 years. *Archives of General Psychiatry, 68,* 1267–1275. http://doi.org/10.1001/archgenpsychiatry.2011.138

Gammon, G. D., & Brown, T. E. (1993). Fluoxetine and methylphenidate in combination for treatment of attention deficit disorder and comorbid depressive disorder. *Journal of Child and Adolescent Psychopharmacology, 3*(1), 1–10. http://doi.org/10.1089/cap.1993.3.1

Garcia, S. P., Guimaraes, J., Zampieri, J. F., Martinez, A. L., Polanczyk, G., & Rohde, L. A. (2009). Response to methylphenidate in children and adolescents with ADHD: does comorbid anxiety disorders matters? *Journal of Neural Transmission, 116,* 631–636. http://doi.org/10.1007/s00702-009-0211-3

Geller, D., Donnelly, C., Lopez, F., Rubin, R., Newcorn, J., Sutton, V., . . . Sumner, C. (2007). Atomoxetine treatment for pediatric patients with attention-deficit/hyperactivity disorder with comorbid anxiety disorder. *Journal of the American Academy of Child and Adolescent Psychiatry, 46,* 1119–1127. http://doi.org/10.1097/chi.0b013e3180ca8385

Gevensleben, H., Holl, B., Albrecht, B., Vogel, C., Schlamp, D., Kratz, O., . . . Heinrich, H. (2009). Is neurofeedback an efficacious treatment for ADHD? A randomised controlled clinical trial. *Journal of Child Psychology and Psychiatry, 50,* 780–789. http://doi.org/10.1111/j.1469-7610.2008.02033.x

Gioia, G. A., Isquith, P. K., Guy, S. C., & Kenworthy, L. (2013). *Behavior Rating Inventory of Executive Function.* Torrance, CA: WPS.

Gol, D., & Jarus, T. (2005). Effect of a social skills training group on everyday activities of children with attention-deficit-hyperactivity disorder. *Developmental Medicine and Child Neurology, 47,* 539–545. http://doi.org/10.1111/j.1469-8749.2005.tb01188.x

Golden, C. J. (1978). *Stroop color and word test manual.* Chicago, IL: Stoelting.

Gordon, M. (1987). How is a computerized attention test used in the diagnosis of attention deficit disorder? *The Young Hyperactive Child, 19,* 53–64.

Grant, D. A., & Berg, E. A. (1948). A behavioural analysis of degree of reinforcement and ease of shifting to new responses in a Weigl-type card sorting problem. *Journal of Experimental Psychology, 38,* 404–411. http://doi.org/10.1037/h0059831

Greenberg, L. M., & Waldman, I. D. (1993). Developmental normative data on the test of variables of attention (T.O.V.A.). *Journal of Child Psychology and Psychiatry, 34,* 1019–1030. http://doi.org/10.1111/j.1469-7610.1993.tb01105.x

Greenhill, L., Kollins, S., Abikoff, H., McCracken, J., Riddle, M., Swanson, J., . . . Cooper, T. (2006). Efficacy and safety of immediate-release methylphenidate treatment for preschoolers with ADHD. *Journal of the American Academy of Child and Adolescent Psychiatry, 45,* 1284–1293. http://doi.org/10.1097/01.chi.0000235077.32661.61

Gresham, F. M., & Elliott, S. N. (1990). *Social Skills Rating System*. Circle Pines, MN: AGS.

Hinshaw, S. P., Owens, E. B., Zalecki, C., Huggins, S. P., Montenegro-Nevado, A. J., Schrodek, E., & Swanson, E. N. (2012). Prospective follow-up of girls with attention-deficit/hyperactivity disorder into early adulthood: continuing impairment includes elevated risk for suicide attempts and self-injury. *Journal of Consulting and Clinical Psychology, 80,* 1041–1051. http://doi.org/10.1037/a0029451

Hoza, B., Gerdes, A. C., Mrug, S., Hinshaw, S. P., Bukowski, W. M., Gold, J. A., . . . Wigal, T. (2005). Peer-assessed outcomes in the multimodal treatment study of children with attention deficit hyperactivity disorder. *Journal of Clinical Child and Adolescent Psychology, 34*(1), 74–86. http://doi.org/10.1207/s15374424jccp3401_7

Humphreys, K. L., Eng, T., & Lee, S. S. (2013). Stimulant medication and substance use outcomes: A meta-analysis. *JAMA Psychiatry, 70,* 740–749. http://doi.org/10.1001/jamapsychiatry.2013.1273

Jensen, P. S., Garcia, J. A., Glied, S., Crowe, M., Foster, M., Schlander, M., . . . Wells, K. (2005). Cost-effectiveness of ADHD treatments: Findings from the multimodal treatment study of children with ADHD. *American Journal of Psychiatry, 162,* 1628–1636. http://doi.org/10.1176/appi.ajp.162.9.1628

Jensen, P. S., Hinshaw, S. P., Kraemer, H. C., Lenora, N., Newcorn, J. H., Abikoff, H. B., . . . Vitiello, B. (2001). ADHD comorbidity findings from the mta study: Comparing comorbid subgroups. *Journal of the American Academy of Child and Adolescent Psychiatry, 40*(2), 147–158. http://doi.org/10.1097/00004583-200102000-00009

Jester, J. M., Nigg, J. T., Adams, K., Fitzgerald, H. E., Puttler, L. I., Wong, M. M., & Zucker, R. A. (2005). Inattention/hyperactivity and aggression from early childhood to adolescence: heterogeneity of trajectories and differential influence of family environment characteristics. *Development and Psychopathology, 17*(1), 99–125. http://doi.org/10.1017/S0954579405050066

Johnston, C., & Mash, E. J. (2001). Families of children with attention-deficit/hyperactivity disorder: review and recommendations for future research. *Clinical Child and Family Psychology Review, 4,* 183–207. http://doi.org/10.1023/A:1017592030434

Kadesjo, B., & Gillberg, C. (2001). The comorbidity of ADHD in the general population of Swedish school-age children. *Journal of Child Psychology and Psychiatry, 42,* 487–492. http://doi.org/10.1111/1469-7610.00742

Kamphaus, R. W., & Reynolds, C. R. (2004). *Behavior Assessment System for Children: Second edition.* Bloomington, MN: Pearson Assessments.

Kessler, R. C., Berglund, P., Demler, O., Jin, R., Merikangas, K. R., & Walters, E. E. (2005). Lifetime prevalence and age-of-onset distributions of DSM-IV disorders in the National Comorbidity Survey Replication. *Archives of General Psychiatry, 62,* 593–602. http://doi.org/10.1001/archpsyc.62.6.617

Kieling, C., Goncalves, R. R. F., Tannock, R., & Castellanos, F. X. (2008). Neurobiology of attention deficit hyperactivity disorder. *Child and Adolescent Psychiatry Clinics of North America, 17,* 285–307. http://doi.org/10.1016/j.chc.2007.11.012

Kieling, C., Kieling, R. R., Rohde, L. A., Frick, P. J., Moffitt, T., Nigg, J. T., . . . Castellanos, F. X. (2010). The age at onset of Attention Deficit Hyperactivity Disorder. *American Journal of Psychiatry, 167*(1), 14–16. http://doi.org/10.1176/appi.ajp.2009.09060796

Klein, S., Ho, V., Tazkarji, B., & Auten, B. (2013). Management of ADHD in preschool-aged children. *American Family Physician, 88,* 398–400.

Knopf, D., Park, M. J., & Mulye, T. P. (2008). *The mental health of adolescents: A national profile,* 2008. San Francisco, CA: National Adolescent Health Information Center, University of California.

Knopik, V. S., Sparrow, E. P., Madden, P. A., Bucholz, K. K., Hudziak, J. J., Reich, W., . . . Heath, A. C. (2005). Contributions of parental alcoholism, prenatal substance exposure, and genetic transmission to child ADHD risk: a female twin study. *Psychological Medicine, 35,* 625–635. http://doi.org/10.1017/S0033291704004155

Kollins, S. H. (2008). ADHD, substance use disorders, and psychostimulant treatment: current literature and treatment guidelines. *Journal of Attention Disorders, 12*(2), 115–125. http://doi.org/10.1177/1087054707311654

Korkman, M., Kirk, U., & Kemp, S. (2007). *NEPSY: Second edition (NEPSY-II)*. San Antonio, TX: Harcourt Assessment.

Kratochvil, C. J., Newcorn, J. H., Arnold, L. E., Duesenberg, D., Emslie, G. J., Quintana, H., . . . Biederman, J. (2005). Atomoxetine alone or combined with fluoxetine for treating ADHD with comorbid depressive or anxiety symptoms. *Journal of the American Academy of Child and Adolescent Psychiatry, 44*, 915–924. http://doi.org/10.1097/01.chi.0000169012.81536.38

Langberg, J. M., & Becker, S. P. (2012). Does long-term medication use improve the academic outcomes of youth with attention-deficit/hyperactivity disorder? *Clinical Child and Family Psychology Review, 15*, 215–233. http://doi.org/10.1007/s10567-012-0117-8

Langberg, J. M., Epstein, J. N., & Graham, A. J. (2008). Organizational-skills interventions in the treatment of ADHD. *Expert Review of Neurotherapeutics, 8*, 1549–1561. http://doi.org/10.1586/14737175.8.10.1549

Langley, K., Holmans, P. A., van den Bree, M. B., & Thapar, A. (2007). Effects of low birth weight, maternal smoking in pregnancy and social class on the phenotypic manifestation of Attention Deficit Hyperactivity Disorder and associated antisocial behaviour: investigation in a clinical sample. *BMC Psychiatry, 7*, 26. http://doi.org/10.1186/1471-244X-7-26

Larson, K., Russ, S. A., Kahn, R. S., & Halfon, N. (2011). *Patterns of comorbidity, functioning, and service use for US children with ADHD*, 2007. *Pediatrics, 127*, 462–470.

Lee, P. C., Niew, W. I., Yang, H. J., Chen, V. C., & Lin, K. C. (2012). A meta-analysis of behavioral parent training for children with attention deficit hyperactivity disorder. *Research in Developmental Disabilities, 33*, 2040–2049. http://doi.org/10.1016/j.ridd.2012.05.011

Lee, S. S., & Humphreys, K. L. (2011). Assessment of attention deficit hyperactivity disorder in young children. In S. W. Evans & B. Hoza (Eds.), *Treating attention deficit hyperactivity disorder: Assessment and intervention in a developmental context*. Kingston, NJ: Civic Research Institute.

Lee, S. S., Humphreys, K. L., Flory, K., Liu, R., & Glass, K. (2011). Prospective association of childhood attention-deficit/hyperactivity disorder (ADHD) and substance use and abuse/dependence: A meta-analytic review. *Clinical Psychology Review, 31*, 328–341. http://doi.org/10.1016/j.cpr.2011.01.006

Lee, S. S., Lahey, B. B., Owens, E. B., & Hinshaw, S. P. (2008). Few preschool boys and girls with ADHD are well-adjusted during adolescence. *Journal of Abnormal Child Psychology, 36*, 373–383. http://doi.org/10.1007/s10802-007-9184-6

LeFever, G. B., Arcona, A. P., & Antonuccio, D. O. (2003). ADHD among American schoolchildren: evidence of overdiagnosis and overuse of medication. *The Scientific Review of Mental Health Practice, 2*, 49–60.

Levy, F., Hay, D. A., Bennett, K. S., & McStephen, M. (2005). Gender differences in ADHD subtype comorbidity. *Journal of the American Academy of Child and Adolescent Psychiatry, 44*, 368–376. http://doi.org/10.1097/01.chi.0000153232.64968.c1

Lezak, M. D. (1995). *Neuropsychological assessment* (3rd ed.). New York: Oxford University Press.

Lifford, K. J., Harold, G. T., & Thapar, A. (2008). Parent-child relationships and ADHD symptoms: a longitudinal analysis. *Journal of Abnormal Child Psychology, 36*, 285–296. http://doi.org/10.1007/s10802-007-9177-5

Lifford, K. J., Harold, G. T., & Thapar, A. (2009). Parent-child hostility and child ADHD symptoms: a genetically sensitive and longitudinal analysis. *Journal of Child Psychology and Psychiatry, 50*, 1468–1476. http://doi.org/10.1111/j.1469-7610.2009.02107.x

Majewicz-Hefley, A., & Carlson, J. S. (2007). A meta-analysis of combined treatments for children diagnosed with ADHD. *Journal of Attention Disorders, 10*, 239–250. http://doi.org/10.1177/1087054706289934

Mannuzza, S., & Klein, R. G. (2000). Long-term prognosis in attention-deficit/hyperactivity disorder. *Child and Adolescent Psychiatric Clinics of North America, 9*, 711–726.

Marcus, S. C., Wan, G. J., Kemner, J. E., & Olfson, M. (2005). Continuity of methylphenidate treatment for atten- tion-deficit/hyperactivity disorder. *Archives of Pediatric and Adolescent Medicine, 159*, 572–578. http://doi.org/10.1001/archpedi.159.9.875

Mautone, J. A., DuPaul, G. J., & Jitendra, A. K. (2005). The effects of computer-assisted instruction on the mathematics performance and classroom behavior of children with ADHD. *Journal of Attention Disorders, 9*(1), 301–312. http://doi.org/10.1177/1087054705278832

McMahon, R. J., & Forehand, R. L. (2003). *Helping the noncompliant child: A clinician's guide to effective parent training.* New York: Guilford Press.

Miller, S., Chang, K. D., & Ketter, T. A. (2013). Bipolar disorder and attention-deficit/hyperactivity disorder comorbidity in children and adolescents: Evidence-based approach to diagnosis and treatment. *Journal of Clinical Psychiatry, 74*(6), 628–629. http://doi.org/10.4088/JCP.13ac08565

Millichap, J. G. (2008). Etiologic classification of attention-deficit/hyperactivity disorder. *Pediatrics, 121*(2), e358–365. http://doi.org/10.1542/peds.2007-1332

Ming, X., Mulvey, M., Mohanty, S., & Patel, V. (2011). Safety and efficacy of clonidine and clonidine extended-release in the treatment of children and adolescents with attention deficit and hyperactivity disorders. *Adolescent Health, Medicine, and Therapeutics, 2*, 105–112. http://doi.org/10.2147/AHMT.S15672

Miranda, A., Presentacion, M. J., & Soriano, M. (2002). Effectiveness of a school-based multicomponent program for the treatment of children with ADHD. *Journal of Learning Disabilities, 35*(6), 546–562. http://doi.org/10.1177/00222194020350060601

Molina, B. S., Hinshaw, S. P., Swanson, J. M., Arnold, L. E., Vitiello, B., Jensen, P. S., . . . MTA Cooperative. Group., (2009). The MTA at 8 years: Prospective follow-up of children treated for combined-type ADHD in a multisite study. *Journal of the American Academy of Child and Adolescent Psychiatry, 48*, 484–500. http://doi.org/10.1097/CHI.0b013e31819c23d0

Molina, B. S. G., Hinshaw, S. P., Swanson, J. M., Arnold, L. E., Vitiello, B., Jensen, P. S., . . . Houck, P. R. (2009). The MTA at 8 years: Prospective follow-up of children treated for combined-type ADHD in a multisite study. *Journal of the American Academy of Child and Adolescent Psychiatry, 48*, 484–500. http://doi.org/10.1097/CHI.0b013e31819c23d0

Montoya, A., Colom, F., & Ferrin, M. (2011). Is psychoeducation for parents and teachers of children and adolescents with ADHD efficacious? A systematic literature review. *European Psychiatry, 26*(3), 166–175. http://doi.org/10.1016/j.eurpsy.2010.10.005

MTA Cooperative Group. (1999). The Multimodal Treatment Study of Children with ADHD: A 14-month randomized clinical trial of treatment strategies for attention-deficit/hyperactivity disorder. *Archives of General Psychiatry, 56*, 1073–1086. http://doi.org/10.1001/archpsyc.56.12.1073

Mulqueen, J. M., Bartley, C. A., & Bloch, M. H. (2013). Meta-analysis: Parental interventions for preschool ADHD. *Journal of Attention Disorders.* Advance online publication. http://doi.org/10.1177/1087054713504135

Nangle, D. W., & Erdley, C. A. (2001). *New directions for child and adolescent development: The role of friendship in psychological adjustment.* San Francisco: Jossey-Bass.

Navarro, J. I., Marchena, E., Alcalde, C., Ruiz, G., Llorens, I., & Aguilar, M. (2003). Improving attention behaviour in primary and secondary school children with a Computer Assisted Instruction procedure. *International Journal of Psychology, 38*, 359–365. http://doi.org/10.1080/00207590244000042

Newcorn, J. H., Halperin, J. M., Jensen, P. S., Abikoff, H. B., Arnold, L. E., Cantwell, D. P., . . . Vitiello, B. (2001). Symptom profiles in children with ADHD: effects of comorbidity and gender. *Journal of the American Academy of Child and Adolescent Psychiatry, 40*(2), 137–146. http://doi.org/10.1097/00004583-200102000-00008

Nigg, J. T., & Barkley, R. A. (2014). Attention-Deficit/Hyperactivity Disorder. In E. J. Mash & R. A. Barkley (Eds.), *Child psychopathology* (3rd ed., pp. 75–144). New York: Guilford Press.

Nigg, J. T., & Casey, B. J. (2005). An integrative theory of attention-deficit/hyperactivity disorder based on the cognitive and affective neurosciences. *Development and Psychopathology, 17*, 785–806.

Nogueira, M., Bosch, R., Valero, S., Gomez-Barros, N., Palomar, G., Richarte, V., . . . Ramos-Quiroga, J. A. (2014). Early-age clinical and developmental features associated to substance use disorders in Attention-Deficit/Hyperactivity Disorder in adults. *Comprehensive Psychiatry, 55*, 639–649. http://doi.org/10.1016/j.comppsych.2013.12.002

Olson, S., Bates, J., Sandy, J., & Lanthier, R. (2000). Early developmental precursors of externalizing behavior in middle childhood and adolescence. *Journal of Abnormal Child Psychology, 28*(2), 119–133. http://doi.org/10.1023/A:1005166629744

Osterrieth, P. A. (1944). Le test de copie d'une figure complexe; contribution à l'étude de la perception et de la mémoire [Test of copying a complex figure: Contribution to the study of perception and memory]. *Archives de Psychologie, 30*, 206–356.

Ota, K. R., & DuPaul, G. J. (2002). Task engagement and mathematics performance in children with attention-deficit hyperactivity disorder: Effects of supplemental computer instruction. *School Psychology Quarterly, 17*, 242–257. http://doi.org/10.1521/scpq.17.3.242.20881

Owens, E. B., Hinshaw, S. P., Kraemer, H. C., Arnold, L. E., Abikoff, H. B., Cantwell, D. P., . . . Wigal, T. (2003). Which treatment for whom for ADHD? Moderators of treatment response in the MTA. *Journal of Consulting and Clinical Psychology, 71*, 540–552. http://doi.org/10.1037/0022-006X.71.3.540

Parker, J., Wales, G., Chalhoub, N., & Harpin, V. (2013). The long-term outcomes of interventions for the management of attention-deficit hyperactivity disorder in children and adolescents: A systematic review of randomized controlled trials. *Psychology Research and Behavior Management, 6*, 87–99. http://doi.org/10.2147/PRBM.S49114

Patel, B. D., & Barzman, D. H. (2013). Pharmacology and pharmacogenetics of pediatric ADHD with associated aggression: a review. *Psychiatric Quarterly, 84*, 407–415. http://doi.org/10.1007/s11126-013-9253-7

Pearl, P. L., Weiss, R. E., & Stein, M. A. (2001). Medical mimics: Medical and neurological conditions simulating ADHD. *Annals of the New York Academy of Sciences, 931*, 97–112. http://doi.org/10.1111/j.1749-6632.2001.tb05775.x

Pelham, W. E., Burrows-Maclean, L., Gnagy, E. M., Fabiano, G. A., Coles, E. K., Tresco, K. E., . . . Hoffman, M. T. (2005). Transdermal methylphenidate, behavioral, and combined treatment for children with ADHD. *Experimental and Clinical Psychopharmacology, 13*(2), 111–126. http://doi.org/10.1037/1064-1297.13.2.111

Pelham, W. E., Fabiano, G. A., Gnagy, E. M., Greiner, A. R., Hoza, B., & Manos, M. J. (2005). The role of summer treatment programs in the context of comprehensive treatment for ADHD. In E. D. Hibbs & P. S. Jensen (Eds.), *Psychosocial treatments for child and adolescent disorders: Empirically based strategies for clinical practice* (2nd ed., pp. 377–410). Washington, DC: APA Press.

Pelham, W. E., Fabiano, G. A., & Massetti, G. M. (2005). Evidence-based assessment of attention deficit hyperactivity disorder in children and adolescents. *Journal of Clinical Child and Adolescent Psychology, 34*, 449–476. http://doi.org/10.1207/s15374424jccp3403_5

Pelham, W. E., & Waschbusch, D. A. (1999). Behavioral interventions in attention deficit/hyperactivity disorder. In H. Quay & A. Hogan (Eds.), *Handbook of disruptive behavior disorders* (pp. 255–278). New York: Kluwer Academic.

Pliszka, S. R., & AACAP Work Group on Quality Issues. (2007). Practice parameter for the assessment and treatment of children and adolescents with attention-deficit/hyperactivity disorder. *Journal of the American Academy of Child and Adolescent Psychiatry, 46*, 894–921 http://doi.org/10.1097/chi.0b013e318054e724

Pliszka, S. R., Crismon, M. L., Hughes, C. W., Corners, C. K., Emslie, G. J., Jensen, P. S., . . . Lopez, M. (2006). Texas Consensus Conference Panel on Pharmacotherapy of Childhood Attention Deficit-Hyperactivity Disorder: The Texas Children's Medication Algorithm Project: Revision of the algorithm for pharmacotherapy of attention-deficit/hyperactivity disorder. *Journal of the American Academy of Child and Adolescent Psychiatry, 45*, 642–657. http://doi.org/10.1097/01.chi.0000215326.51175.eb

Polanczyk, G. V., de Lima, M. S., Horta, B. L., Biederman, J., & Rohde, L. A. (2007). The worldwide prevalence of ADHD: a systematic review and metaregression analysis. *American Journal of Psychiatry, 164*, 942–948. http://doi.org/10.1176/appi.ajp.164.6.942

Polanczyk, G. V., Willcutt, E. G., Salum, G. A., Kieling, C., & Rohde, L. A. (2014). ADHD prevalence estimates across three decades: an updated systematic review and meta-regression analysis. *International Journal of Epidemiology.* Advance online publication. http://doi.org/10.1093/ije/dyt261

Quinlan, D. M. (2000). Assessment of attention-deficit/hyperactivity disorder and comorbidities. In T. E. Brown (Ed.), *Attention-deficit disorders and comorbidities in children, adolescents, and adults* (pp. 455–508). Washington, DC: American Psychiatric Press.

Raggi, V. L., & Chronis, A. M. (2006). Interventions to address the academic impairment of children and adolescents with ADHD. *Clinical Child and Family Psychology Review, 9*(2), 85–111. http://doi.org/10.1007/s10567-006-0006-0

Raishevich-Cunningham, N., & Jensen, P. (2011). Attention-deficit/ hyperactivity disorder. In R. M. Kliegman, B. M. D. Stanton, J. St. Geme, N. F. Schor, & R. E. Behrman (Eds.), *Nelson textbook of pediatrics* (19th ed., pp. 108–111). Philadelphia, PA: Saunders.

Reich, W., Welner, Z., & Herjanic, B. (2000). *Diagnostic Interview for Children and Adolescents-IV (DICA-IV)*. New York: Multi-Health Systems.

Reiff, M. I., & Tippins, S. (2004). *ADHD: A complete and authoritative guide*. Oak Grove Village, IL: American Association of Pediatrics.

Reynolds, C. R., & Kamphaus, R. W. (2004). *Behavior assessment system for children* (2nd ed.). Circle Pines, MN: American Guidance Service.

Robbins, T. W., James, M., Owen, A. M., Sahakian, B. J., McInnes, L., & Rabbitt, P. (1994). Cambridge Neuropsychological Test Automated Battery (CANTAB): A factor analytic study of a large sample of normal elderly volunteers. *Dementia, 5*, 266–281.

Rodriguez, A., Olsen, J., Kotimaa, A. J., Kaakinen, M., Moilanen, I., Henriksen, T. B., . . . Jarvelin, M. R. (2009). Is prenatal alcohol exposure related to inattention and hyperactivity symptoms in children? Disentangling the effects of social adversity. *Journal of Child Psychology and Psychiatry, 50*, 1073–1083. http://doi.org/10.1111/j.1469-7610.2009.02071.x

Rugino, T. A., & Samsock, T. C. (2003). Modafinil in children with attention-deficit hyperactivity disorder. *Pediatric Neurology, 29*(2), 136–142. http://doi.org/10.1016/S0887-8994(03)00148-6

Scheffer, R. E., Kowatch, R. A., Carmody, T., & Rush, A. J. (2005). Randomized, placebo-controlled trial of mixed amphetamine salts for symptoms of comorbid ADHD in pediatric bipolar disorder after mood stabilization with divalproex sodium. *American Journal of Psychiatry, 162*(1), 58–64. http://doi.org/10.1176/appi.ajp.162.1.58

Shaffer, D., Fisher, P., Lucas, C. P., Dulcan, M. K., & Schwab-Stone, M. E. (2000). NIMH Diagnostic Interview Schedule for Children Version IV (NIMH DISC-IV): Description, differences from previous versions, and reliability of some common diagnoses. *Journal of American Academy of Child and Adolescent Psychiatry, 39*(1), 28–38. http://doi.org/10.1097/00004583-200001000-00014

Shaw, M., Hodgkins, P., Caci, H., Young, S., Kahle, J., Woods, A. G., & Arnold, L. E. (2012). A systematic review and analysis of long-term outcomes in attention deficit hyperactivity disorder: Effects of treatment and non-treatment. *BMC Medicine, 10*, 99–114. http://doi.org/10.1186/1741-7015-10-99

Shaw, R., & Lewis, V. (2005). The impact of computer-mediated and traditional academic task presentation on the performance and behaviour of children with ADHD. *Journal of Research in Special Educational Needs, 5*(2), 47–54. http://doi.org/10.1111/J.1471-3802.2005.00041.x

Shepard, B. A., Carter, A. S., & Cohen, J. E. (2000). Attention-deficit/hyperactivity disorder and the preschool child. In T. E. Brown (Ed.), *Attention-deficit disorders and comorbidities in children, adolescents, and adults* (pp. 407–436). Washington, DC: American Psychiatric Publishing.

Shier, A. C., Reichenbacher, T., Ghuman, H. S., & Ghuman, J. K. (2013). Pharmacological treatment of attention deficit hyperactivity disorder in children and adolescents: Clinical strategies. *Journal of Central Nervous System Disease, 5*, 1–17

Shulman, G. L., Fiez, J. A., Corbetta, M., Buckner, R. L., Miezin, F. M., Raichle, M. E., & Petersen, S. E. (1997). Common blood flow changes across visual tasks: Decreases in cerebral cortex. *Journal of Cognitive Neuroscience, 9*, 648–663. http://doi.org/10.1162/jocn.1997.9.5.648

Sibley, M. H., Kuriyan, A. B., Evans, S. W., Waxmonsky, J. G., & Smith, B. H. (2014). Pharmacological and psychosocial treatments for adolescents with ADHD: An updated systematic review of the literature. *Clinical Psychology Review, 34*, 218–232. http://doi.org/10.1016/j.cpr.2014.02.001

Silverman, W. K., & Hinshaw, S. P. (2008). The second special issue on evidence-based psychosocial treatments for children and adolescents: A 10-year update. *Journal of Clinical Child & Adolescent Psychology, 37*(1), 1–7. http://doi.org/10.1080/15374410701818293

Sinha, G. (2005). Training the brain: Cognitive therapy as an alternative to ADHD drugs. *Scientific American, 293*(1), 22–23. http://doi.org/10.1038/scientificamerican0705-22

Solanto, M. V., Arnsten, A. F. T., & Castellanos, F. X. (2001). *Stimulant drugs and ADHD: Basic and clinical neuroscience*. New York: Oxford University Press.

Sonuga-Barke, E. J. S., & Castellanos, F. X. (2007). Spontaneous attentional fluctuations in impaired states and pathological conditions: A neurobiological hypothesis. *Neuroscience and Biobehavioral Reviews, 31,* 977–986. http://doi.org/10.1016/j.neubiorev.2007.02.005

Sparrow, E. P., & Erhardt, D. (2014). *Essentials of ADHD assessment for children and adolescents*. Hoboken, NJ: Wiley.

Sparrow, S. S., Cicchetti, D. V., & Balla, D. A. (2005). *Vineland Adaptive Behavior Scales* (2nd ed.). Circle Pines, MN: AGS.

Spencer, T., Wilens, T., Biederman, J., Wozniak, J., & Harding-Crawford, M. (2000). Attention-deficit/hyperactivity disorder with mood disorders. In T. E. Brown (Ed.), *Attention deficit disorders and comorbidities in children, adolescents, and adults* (pp. 79–124). Washington, DC: American Psychiatric Press.

Spies, R. A., Carlson, J. F., & Geisinger, K. F. (2010). *The eighteenth mental measurements yearbook*. Lincoln, NE: Buros Institute of Mental Measurements.

St. Sauver, J. L., Barbaresi, W. J., Katusic, S. K., Colligan, R. C., Weaver, A. L., & Jacobsen, S. J. (2004). Early life risk factors for attention-deficit/hyperactivity disorder: A population-based cohort study. *Mayo Clinic Proceedings, 79,* 1124–1131. http://doi.org/10.1016/S0025-6196(11)62594-9

Swanson, J., Baler, R. D., & Volkow, N. D. (2011). Understanding the effects of stimulant medications on cognition in individuals with Attention-Deficit Hyperactivity Disorder: A decade of progress. *Neuropsychopharmacology, 36*(1), 207–226. http://doi.org/10.1038/npp.2010.160

Swanson, J. M. (1992). *The SNAP-IV Teacher and Parent Rating Scale: School-based assessments and interventions for ADD students*. Irvine, CA: KC.

Swanson, J. M., Kraemer, H. C., Hinshaw, S. P., Arnold, L. E., Conners, C. K., Abikoff, H. B., . . . Wu, M. (2001). Clinical relevance of the primary findings of the MTA: success rates based on severity of ADHD and ODD symptoms at the end of treatment. *Journal of the American Academy of Child and Adolescent Psychiatry, 40*(2), 168–179. http://doi.org/10.1097/00004583-200102000-00011

Tannock, R., & Brown, T. E. (2000). Attention-deficit disorders with learning disorders in children and adolescents. In T. E. Brown (Ed.), *Attention deficit disorders and comorbidities in children, adolescents, and adults* (pp. 231–296). Washington, DC: American Psychiatric Press.

Tannock, R., Ickowicz, A., & Schachar, R. (1995). Differential effects of methylphenidate on working memory in ADHD children with and without comorbid anxiety. *Journal of the American Academy of Child and Adolescent Psychiatry, 34,* 886–896. http://doi.org/10.1097/00004583-199507000-00012

Taylor, E. (2011). Antecedents of ADHD: A historical account of diagnostic concepts. *Attention Deficit and Hyperactivity Disorders, 3*(2), 69–75. http://doi.org/10.1007/s12402-010-0051-x

Thapar, A., Cooper, M., Eyre, O., & Langley, K. (2013). What have we learnt about the causes of ADHD? *Journal of Child Psychology and Psychiatry, 54*(1), 3–16. http://doi.org/10.1111/j.1469-7610.2012.02611.x

Tourette's Syndrome Study Group. (2002). Treatment of ADHD in children with tics: A randomized controlled trial. *Neurology, 58*(4), 527–536.

Tripp, G., & Wickens, J. R. (2008). Research review: Dopamine transfer deficit: A neurobiological theory of altered reinforcement mechanisms in ADHD. *Journal of Child Psychology and Psychiatry, 49,* 691–704. http://doi.org/10.1111/j.1469-7610.2007.01851.x

Tripp, G., & Wickens, J. R. (2009). Neurobiology of ADHD. *Neuropharmacology, 57,* 579–589. http://doi.org/10.1016/j.neuropharm.2009.07.026

van der Oord, S., Ponsioen, A. J. G. B., Geurts, H. M., Brink, E. L. T., & Prins, P. J. M. (2014). A pilot study of the efficacy of a computerized executive functioning remediation training with game elements for children with ADHD in an outpatient setting: Outcome on parent- and teacher-rated executive functioning and ADHD behavior. *Journal of Attention Disorders, 18,* 699–712. http://doi.org/10.1177/1087054712453167

Van der Oord, S., Prins, P. J., Oosterlaan, J., & Emmelkamp, P. M. (2008). Efficacy of methylphenidate, psychosocial treatments and their combination in school-aged children with ADHD: a meta-analysis. *Clinical Psychology Review, 28,* 783–800. http://doi.org/10.1016/j.cpr.2007.10.007

Visser, S. N., Danielson, M. L., Bitsko, R. H., Holbrook, J. R., Kogan, M. D., Ghandour, R. M., . . . Blumberg, S. J. (2014). Trends in the parent-report of health care provider-diagnosed and medicated attention-deficit/hyperactivity disorder: United states, 2003–2011. *Journal of the American Academy of Child and Adolescent Psychiatry, 53*(1), 34–46. http://doi.org/10.1016/j.jaac.2013.09.001

Visser, S. N., Lesesne, C. A., & Perou, R. (2007). National estimates and factors associated with medication treatment for childhood attention-deficit/hyperactivity disorder. *Pediatrics, 119*(1), S99–S106. http://doi.org/10.1542/peds.2006-2089O

Volkow, N. D., Fowler, J. S., Wang, G., Ding, Y., & Gatley, S. J. (2002). Mechanism of action of methylphenidate: insights from PET imaging studies. *Journal of Attention Disorders, 6*(1), S31–S43.

Waschbusch, D. A. (2002). A meta-analytic examination of comorbid hyperactive-impulsive-attention problems and conduct problems. *Psychological Bulletin, 128*(1), 118–150. http://doi.org/10.1037/0033-2909.128.1.118

Wechsler, D. (2004). *Wechsler Intelligence Scale for Children – 4th edition (WISC-IV)*. London: Pearson.

Weersing, V. R., & Weisz, J. R. (2002). Mechanisms of action in youth psychotherapy. *Journal of Child Psychology and Psychiatry, 43*(1), 3–29. http://doi.org/10.1111/1469-7610.00002

Weiss, M., Hechtman, L. T., & Weiss, G. (1999). *ADHD in adulthood: A guide to current theory, diagnosis, and treatment*. Baltimore, MD: Johns Hopkins University Press.

Wells, K. C., Chi, T. C., Hinshaw, S. P., Epstein, J. N., Pfiffner, L., Nebel-Schwalm, M., . . . Wigal, T. (2006). Treatment-related changes in objectively measured parenting behaviors in the multimodal treatment study of children with attention-deficit/hyperactivity disorder. *Journal of Consulting and Clinical Psychology, 74,* 649–657. http://doi.org/10.1037/0022-006X.74.4.649

Wilens, T. E. (2006). Attention deficit hyperactivity disorder and substance use disorders. *American Journal of Psychiatry, 163,* 2059–2063. http://doi.org/10.1176/appi.ajp.163.12.2059

Wilens, T. E., Adamson, J., Monuteaux, M. C., Faraone, S. V., Schillinger, M., Westerberg, D., & Biederman, J. (2008). Effect of prior stimulant treatment for attention-deficit/hyperactivity disorder on subsequent risk for cigarette smoking and alcohol and drug use disorders in adolescents. *Archives of Pediatric & Adolescent Medicine, 162,* 916–921. http://doi.org/10.1001/archpedi.162.10.916

Wilens, T. E., Spencer, T. J., & Biederman, J. (2000). Attention-deficit/hyperactivity disorder with substance abuse disorders. In T. E. Brown (Ed.), *Attention deficit disorders and comorbidities in children, adolescents, and adults* (pp. 319–339). Washington, DC: American Psychiatric Press.

Williamson, D., Murray, D. W., Damaraju, C. V., Ascher, S., & Starr, H. L. (2014). Methylphenidate in children with ADHD with or without learning disability. *Journal of Attention Disorders, 18*(2), 95–104. http://doi.org/10.1177/1087054712443411

Wolraich, M. L., Brown, L., Brown, R. T., DuPaul, G. J., Earls, M., Feldman, H. M., . . . Visser, S. (2011). ADHD: Clinical practice guideline for the diagnosis, evaluation, and treatment of Attention-Deficit/Hyperactivity Disorder in children and adolescents. *Pediatrics, 128,* 1007–1022. http://doi.org/10.1542/peds.2011-2654

Wolraich, M. L., Lambert, E. W., Bickman, L., Simmons, T., Doffing, M. A., & Worley, K. A. (2004). Assessing the impact of parent and teacher agreement on diagnosing attention-deficit hyperactivity disorder. *Journal of Developmental and Behavioral Pediatrics, 25*(1), 41–47. http://doi.org/10.1097/00004703-200402000-00007

Wolraich, M. L., Lambert, W., Doffing, M. A., Bickman, L., Simmons, T., & Worley, K. (2003). Psychometric properties of the Vanderbilt ADHD diagnostic parent rating scale in a referred population. *Journal of Pediatric Psychology, 28,* 559–567. http://doi.org/10.1093/jpepsy/jsg046

Woodcock, R. W., McGrew, K. S., & Mather, N. (2001). *The Woodcock Johnson Tests of Achievement.* Rolling Meadows, IL: Riverside Publishing.

World Health Organization. (2014). *International classification of diseases, tenth revision, clinical modification.* Geneva: Author.

Zito, J. M., Safer, D. J., Valluri, S., Gardner, J. F., Korelitz, J. J., & Mattison, D. R. (2007). Psychotherapeutic medication prevalence in Medicaid-insured preschoolers. *Journal of Child and Adolescent Psychopharmacology, 17,* 195–203. http://doi.org/10.1089/cap.2007.0006

Zuvekas, S. H., & Vitiello, B. (2012). Stimulant medication use in children: A 12-year perspective. *The American Journal of Psychiatry, 169,* 160–166. http://doi.org/10.1176/appi.ajp.2011.11030387

8

Appendix: Tools and Resources

Appendix 1: Support Groups and Organizations
Appendix 2: Toolkits and Rating Scales

Support Groups and Organizations

The Attention Deficit Information Network, Inc. (Ad-IN)
475 Hillside Ave.
Needham, MA 02194
USA
Tel. +1 781 455-9895
Provides information for families of children and adults with ADHD. Offers aid in finding solutions to practical problems faced by patients and families, as well as professionals through a network of Ad-IN chapters.

ADD Warehouse
3200 Northwest 70th Ave., Suite 102
Plantation, FL 33317
USA
Tel. +1 800 233-9273
http://www.addwarehouse.com
A central location for ordering books, tapes, assessment scales, and videos selected to help parents, educators, and health professional assist people affected by developmental disorders and ADHD.

Center for Mental Health Services
5600 Fishers Lane, Rm 15–105
Rockville, MD 20857
USA
Tel. +1 800 789-2647
http://www.samhsa.gov
A branch of the US Department of Health and Human Services that provides a range of information on mental health, treatment, and support services.

Children and Adults With Attention-Deficit/Hyperactivity Disorder (CHADD)
CHADD National Office
4601 Presidents Drive, Suite 300
Lanham, MD 20706
USA
Tel. +1 800 233-4050
http://www.chadd.org
This national nonprofit organization provides education, advocacy, and support for individuals with ADHD. In addition to CHADD's informative website, it also publishes a variety of printed materials, including *Attention* magazine, a free newsletter, and other publications, on research advances and treatments for ADHD.

Council for Exceptional Children
1110 North Glebe Rd., Suite 300
Arlington, VA 22201-5704
USA
Tel. +1 888 232-7733
http://www.cec.sped.org

The CEC is the largest international professional organization dedicated to improving educational outcomes for individuals with disabilities and/or gifts and talents. It supplies materials for educators working with children.

National Federation of Families for Children's Mental Health
9605 Medical Center Dr., Suite 280
Rockville, MD
USA
Tel. +1 240 403-1901
http://www.ffcmh.org
This national, family-run organization links more than 120 chapters and state organizations that serve the needs of children with emotional, behavioral, and mental health needs and their families. The federation provides publications and information on related seminars and workshops, and it hosts a speaker's bureau and crisis intervention and support groups.

HEATH Resource Center at the National Youth Transitions Center
Graduate School of Education and Human Development
The George Washington University
2134 G Street, NW
Washington, DC 20052-0001
USA
Tel. +1 202 994-8860
http://heath.gwu.edu/
This center serves as a national clearinghouse on postsecondary education for individuals with disabilities, and provides information on educational resources, support services, and financial aid for students with disabilities, including federal aid, state vocational rehabilitation services, and regional and local sources.

National Center for Learning Disabilities (NCLD)
381 Park Ave. South, Suite 1401
New York, NY 10016
USA
Tel. +1 212 545-7510 or +1 888 575-7373
http://www.ld.org
The NCLD offers information and referral services and advocates for more effective policies related to learning disabilities. It connects parents with essential resources, provides educators with evidence-based tools, and engages advocates in public policy initiatives.

National Information Center for Children and Youth With Disabilities (NICHCY)
P.O. Box 1492
Washington, DC 20013
USA
Tel. +1 800 695-0285
http://www.nichcy.org
This center provides information about disabilities in children and youths, including programs and services for infants, children, and youths with disabilities, special education laws, and research on effective practices for children with disabilities. It also lists resources in every state, including parenting training and information centers.

National Institute of Mental Health (NIMH)
6001 Executive Blvd.
Rockville, MD 20852
Tel. +1 301 443-4513 or +1 866 615-6464
http://www.nimh.nih.gov
A comprehensive resource for information based on research advances in brain, behavior, and mental illness. Provides information on ADHD assessment, diagnosis, treatment, and clinical trials.

National Attention Deficit Disorder Association (ADDA)
PO Box 103,
Denver, PA 17517
USA
Tel. +1 800 939-1019
E-mail: info@add.org
http://www.add.org/
This association provides information, resources, webinars and networking opportunities for adults impacted by ADHD, and for the professionals that work with these individuals.

US Department of Education Office of Special Education Programs (OSEP)
400 Maryland Ave. SW
Washington, DC 20202
USA
Tel. +1 800 872-5327
http://www.ed.gov/about/offices/list/osers/osep/index.html
The OSEP is dedicated to providing leadership and financial support to assist states and local districts in serving youth with disabilities. The OSEP has an excellent site for information on parent training and information centers.

Toolkits

American Academy of Pediatrics
Caring for Children with ADHD: A Resource Toolkit for Clinicians (2nd edition)
141 Northwest Point Blvd.
Elk Grove, IL 60007
USA
Tel. +1 847 434-4000
http://shop.aap.org/Caring-for-Children-with-ADHD-A-Resource-Toolkit-for-Clinicians/
This toolkit is based on the revised ADHD treatment guidelines published by the American Academy of Pediatrics in 2009. The toolkit provides resources for clinicians for understanding and treating children with ADHD. More than 40 tools are provided to help clinicians deliver services to children and their family members. The current retail price is $94.95.

Center for Children & Families at the State University of New York, University at Buffalo
ADHD fact sheets, treatment programs, and assessment instruments for parents, teachers, mental health professionals, and students.
106 Diefendorf Hall
3435 Main Street
Buffalo, NY 14214
USA
Tel. +1 716 829-2244
http://ccf.buffalo.edu/resources_downloads.php#GR
This website provides an abundance of free and valuable resources for parents, educators, professionals, and students. These resources include fact sheets, treatment materials, and assessment instruments.

Rating Scales

Instrument name: **The Swanson, Nolan, and Pelham Rating Scale-Revised** (SNAP-IV), by James M. Swanson, PhD, University of California, Irvine, is consistent with the DSM-IV-TR and its diagnostic criteria for ADHD. The SNAP-IV is a 90-item questionnaire to be completed by teachers and caregivers, requiring approximately 10 min. The scale is designed to help practitioners assess children between the ages of 6 and 18 based on teacher and caregiver report.
The SNAP-IV is a free resource that can be accessed at http://www.forabrighterfuture.com/pdf/SNAP-IVTeacherParetnRatingScale.pdf

Instrument name: **Vanderbilt ADHD Diagnostic Parent and Teacher Rating Scale.** These scales are designed for use with children ages 6 to 12 years. Approximate time to complete is 10 min.
The teacher form can be accessed at http://www.brightfutures.org/mentalhealth/pdf/professionals/bridges/adhd.pdf
The parent form can be accessed at http://www.childrenshospital.vanderbilt.org/uploads/documents/DIAGNOSTIC_PARENT_RATING_SCALE%281%29.pdf

Also available in the series:

Attention-Deficit / Hyperactivity Disorder in Adults

by Brian P. Daly, Elizabeth Nicholls, and Ronald T. Brown

ISBN: 978-0-88937-413-3
Advances in Psychotherapy – Evidence-Based Practice, Vol. 35
2016, ca. 122 pp.
Regular price: US $29.80 / € 24.95 / £ 19.90
Prices for APA Division 12 and 42 members: US $24.80 / € 19.95 / £ 15.90
Prices correct as of August 2015 (subject to change).

Compact and authoritative guidance on evidence-based treatment for ADHD in adults

Attention-Deficit/Hyperactivity Disorder (ADHD) is a neurodevelopmental disorder that emerges during childhood. However, it is now well recognized that ADHD frequently persists over the lifespan and well into adulthood. Although ADHD is typically first identified during the childhood years, the presentation of symptoms may differ considerably between adults and children. Without appropriate symptom management, ADHD can significantly interfere with academic, emotional, social, and work functioning. When properly identified and diagnosed, however, outcomes in adults with ADHD who receive appropriate treatment are encouraging.

This volume in the *Advances in Psychotherapy* series is both a compact "how to" reference, for use by professional clinicians in their daily work, and an ideal educational reference for practice-oriented students. The most important feature of this volume is that it is practical and reader friendly.

It has a similar structure to others in the series, and is a compact and easy to follow guide covering all aspects of practice that are relevant in real life in the assessment and management of ADHD in adults. Tables, relevant case studies, and marginal notes assist orientation, while suggestions for further reading, support groups, and educational organizations are provided for individuals and professionals.

Date Due

BRODART, CO.   Cat. No. 23-233   Printed in U.S.A.